GLASGOW UNIVERSITY PUBLICATIONS

•

STUDIES
ON
LOCH LOMOND
II

•

THE FAUNA OF THE RIVER ENDRICK

STUDIES ON
LOCH LOMOND
II

•

THE FAUNA OF
THE RIVER ENDRICK

by PETER S. MAITLAND, B.Sc., Ph.D.

•

PUBLISHED FOR
THE UNIVERSITY OF GLASGOW
BY BLACKIE & SON LIMITED
1966

BLACKIE & SON LIMITED
5 FITZHARDINGE STREET
PORTMAN SQUARE
LONDON · W.I
BISHOPBRIGGS, GLASGOW

BLACKIE & SON
(INDIA) LIMITED
103-5 FORT STREET
BOMBAY

Printed in Great Britain by Blackie & Son Ltd., Glasgow

CONTENTS

Contents

INTRODUCTION

The great dearth of river surveys in Great Britain has been emphasized by Hynes (1959 and 1960) who noted (1960) that "a task which is of immediate importance is an accurate scientific survey of the biological condition of all bodies of water which are liable to damage by pollution or engineering works". The situation in Scotland is even worse than elsewhere, for, until recently, little research had ever been carried out here comparable to the valuable studies in Wales by Carpenter (1927), Jones (1940, etc.), Badcock (1949) and Hynes (1961); those in England by Percival and Whitehead (1929), Butcher, Pentelow and Woodley (1930), and Moon (1937, etc.); and those in Ireland by Frost (1939, etc.).

The present account of the River Endrick is the outcome of a series of studies carried out on this river from 1959 to 1963. Some of this research has already been published in detail elsewhere (Maitland, 1962a, 1962b, 1963, 1964a, 1964b and 1965); most of this is presented here in summary form only. The attempt has been made to give a balanced account of the River Endrick as a whole, but it is obvious that there are certain insufficiencies—particularly with regard to lack of information concerning the flora of this river, but also in connection with certain aspects of the fish and invertebrate fauna. It is hoped that future research may remedy these deficiencies.

I am grateful to Professor C. M. Yonge, C.B.E., F.R.S., for the facilities provided for this research in the Department of Zoology at the University of Glasgow. Dr. H. D. Slack, F.R.S.E., was kind enough to give his advice at various stages of the work, and I am grateful to him for this encouragement. Grateful thanks are also acknowledged to Professor W. Russell Hunter, F.R.S.E., and Dr. T. A. Stuart, F.R.S.E., for discussing many aspects of river ecology, particularly in the early stages of this research; Mr. P. K. H. Yeoh too was kind enough to discuss several points with me.

Much of the field work was carried out with the help of my wife,

Kathleen; I am indebted to her for this, and also for her help with the checking of the manuscript. Information for assessing the influence of man on the fauna of the River Endrick was kindly supplied by a number of people and among these I would thank especially Mr. E. W. Denholm, Mr. J. O. Stewart, and Mr. T. Nisbit; I am very grateful also to Mr. J. H. Spencer for permitting me to publish certain chemical data included in this study (Fig. 22B; Tables 5, 18 and 21). Permission to work on parts of the River Endrick under their control was generously given by Mr. A. B. Davidson, Mr. R. A. Hay and Mr. E. A. Maxwell.

The receipt of a Scholarship from the Carnegie Trust for the Universities of Scotland during the years 1959 to 1962 is gratefully acknowledged, as is the provision of transport in connection with field work during the same period by the Loch Lomond Angling Improvement Association.

Much of the research described in the present study is to a large extent dependent on the accurate identification of the different invertebrate species occurring in the River Endrick. Whilst all the initial identifications were carried out by the author, several zoologists were kind enough to help with the difficult groups and the identity of most species has now been established. It is with sincere thanks that I acknowledge the help of the following: Dr. T. B. Reynoldson (Tricladida), Dr. Christina Sperber (Naididae), Mr. C. R. Kennedy (Tubificidae), Dr. K. H. Mann (Hirudinea), Dr. W. P. Harding (Entomostraca), Dr. I. M. Gordon (*Bathynella*), Mr. G. M. Spooner (*Gammarus*), Dr. T. T. Macan (Ephemeroptera nymphs), Dr. H. B. N. Hynes (Plecoptera nymphs), Dr. A. R. Waterston (Hemiptera), Dr. D. E. Kimmins (Trichoptera adults), Miss R. M. Badcock (Hydropsychidae larvae), Dr. J. M. Edington (Philopotamidae and Polycentropidae larvae), Dr. L. Davies (Simuliidae larvae and pupae), Dr. P. Freeman (Chironomidae adults), Dr. R. A. Crowson (Coleoptera), Mr. T. Gledhill (Hydracarina) and Professor W. Russell Hunter (Mollusca).

The present condition of the River Endrick is for the most part a natural one, as it is hoped that this study will show. The recent establishment by the Nature Conservancy of the Loch Lomond National Nature Reserve, which includes part of the lower reaches

of the River Endrick, and also the very valuable work being undertaken in the area by the Clyde River Purification Board, should help
towards maintaining (and perhaps even improving) this condition in
the future. It would be pleasant to think that anyone writing of this
river 300 years hence might still recall it as favourably as did Franck
in 1658, when he wrote of "The memorable Anderwick, a rapid river
of strong and stiff streams; whose fords, if well examined, are argu-
ments sufficient to convince the angler of trout; as are her deeps,
when consulted, the noble race and treasure of salmon".

PETER S. MAITLAND

Department of Zoology,
University of Glasgow.
October, 1964.

I. The River Endrick

Geology

The solid geology of the Endrick valley, in broad outline at least, is relatively simple and is illustrated in Fig. 1. The oldest rocks of the area are the Dalradian slates, quartzites and schists which lie to the north of the Highland Boundary Fault Line traversing Scotland from east to west (Bassett, 1958). Only a small part of these, however, lies within the Endrick valley, in the extreme north-west.

The succeeding Old Red Sandstone covers much of the rest of the valley, and as a group contains not only great thicknesses of lacustrine sediments but also some volcanic lavas and associated igneous intrusions. To the south of the Highland Boundary Fault Line, the lower Old Red Sandstone dips southward in a belt some 8 km. wide, reappearing in the cone of an anticline near Killearn (Fig. 1). The faulted contact between the upper and lower Old Red Sandstone is not readily visible on the surface, due to a covering of glacial deposit material, but it is well exposed by the River Endrick at the Pot of Gartness—an important waterfall of which the significance to the biology of the river will be discussed below. At this point the lower Old Red Sandstone dips gently upstream, and one of its members more resistant than the others gives rise to the waterfall. The upper Old Red Sandstone follows the lower without obvious transgression, and the river affords a fine section of it in Finnich Glen, where the Finnich Burn has cut a deep gorge through the rock, this chasm being in some places over 25 m. deep.

South of the Old Red Sandstone is the Calciferous Sandstone series known as the Ballagan Group, consisting of alternations of thin-bedded soft shales and fine-grained impure dolomitic limestones with some micaceous sandstone beds. On top of these Ballagan sandstones lies the mass of basaltic lavas comprising the chief hills of the area, the Campsie Fells. These lavas consist of many flows laid down

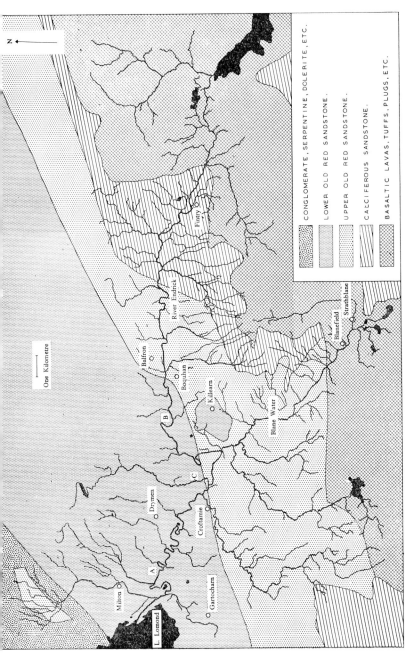

Fig. 1.—A simplified geological map of the Endrick valley showing the main centres of population and the three stations (A, B, and C) where quantitative studies were carried out

one on top of the other, the whole mass dipping gently to the south-east. The highest point flanking the area—Earl's Seat (578 m.)—is found here. The Fintry Hills are essentially a continuation of the Campsie Fells in the north, whilst the Kilpatrick Hills to the south-west are also formed from basaltic lavas (Fig. 2). Isolated steep hills in this region mark the presence of old volcanic vents, the most out-standing of which, and probably the most characteristic landmark in the whole valley, is the hill of Dumgoyne.

Morainic glacial deposits form a veneer over much of the low ground in the Endrick valley. The major effect of glaciation in the area has been the scraping away of unconsolidated material from the tops of surrounding hills, and its subsequent deposition in the valley below (Clough, 1925). Thus much of the valley floor is covered with boulder clay, alluvial sands, gravels and morainic deposits. That this is mainly derived from the rocks of the Old Red Sandstone is indi-cated by the predominant red colouration of this drift. As discussed below, some of these deposits may be of great importance in the distribution and occurrence of certain species of animals which are interstitial in habit, e.g. *Bathynella natans* (Maitland, 1962*a*), and on their quality the productivity of the River Endrick itself must also to a large extent depend.

Development

The past history of flow of the River Endrick affords an interesting example of river development, and may well be of importance when considering the geographical relationships and distribution of the present aquatic fauna of waters on the east and west coasts of Scot-land. Though the present drainage of the area is to the west via the River Endrick and Loch Lomond, this was not always so. The Campsie Fells and other hills in the area had at one time no topo-graphical identity but were a portion of an upland tract probably continuous with the Highlands to the north (Clough, 1925). Gradu-ally the forces of erosion picked out the present landscape, and the differential qualities of resistance between the soft sedimentary rocks and the more resistant igneous rocks caused the formation of a valley along the foot of the north face of the latter which were left up-

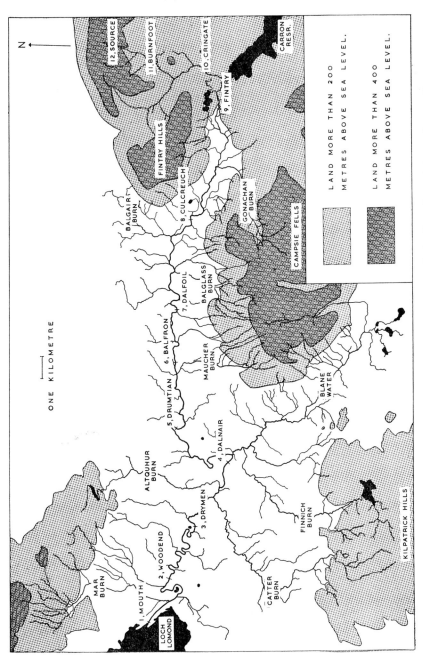

Fig. 2.—A contour map of the Endrick valley showing the principal tributaries and the stations on the main river where qualitative collections of the invertebrate fauna were made

standing as an erosional scarp. The drainage of this valley was originally to the east through the Carron valley to the Firth of Forth, and it would appear that the drainage of much of the surrounding region was in this direction also. Subsequent erosion and tilting of the Scottish landmass, however, altered this drainage to cause the River Endrick to drain to the Clyde via Loch Lomond and the River Leven. Remaining indications of this past flow of water are found in the many wind gaps present in the area, notable among such being the through, high-level valley connecting the Endrick and Carron valleys, and now occupied by Carron Reservoir (Fig. 2). All these readjustments were essentially complete in pre-glacial times, and the effect of glaciation on relief and drainage in the area was to modify, but not materially alter, this pattern.

Topography

The watershed of the River Endrick lies almost entirely within the Midland Valley of Scotland. The river rises at a height of just under 500 m. above sea-level some 56 km. north-east of Glasgow, and flows mostly westward through a distance of 49 km. to enter Loch Lomond in its south-east corner. It has a catchment area of about 26,700 hectares and is by far the largest river flowing into Loch Lomond—of which the entire drainage area is less than 71,300 hectares (Slack, 1957a). From Loch Lomond the waters of the Endrick find their way to the sea via the River Leven and the River Clyde; essentially therefore the Endrick valley forms part of the Clyde watershed.

The source of the River Endrick is in the Gargunnock Hills in Stirlingshire. Several small streams rising in this area flow over a rather soft substrate of peat on high treeless moorland before joining to form the main river. Smith (1896) states that the River Endrick is formed by the confluence of the Gourlay and Burnfoot Burns, but for the purposes of the present account the source of the river is taken as the start of the highest rising tributary in this area (Fig. 2), known locally as Mary Glyn's Burn. Below the stretch of peat, the bed of the river becomes rocky, much of this being bare solid rock at first, but soon loose boulders and stones appear and these cover much of the river bed. The current in this stretch is fast and there are many waterfalls over 2 m. high and also many pools of about that depth. Gradually the gradient of the river eases somewhat and the bottom consists for the most part of large moss-covered boulders and smaller stones. Most of the land in this area is bare moorland used for rough grazing, though as mentioned below some of the slopes near Carron Reservoir have now been planted with conifers.

At the Loup of Fintry, the highest waterfall in the river is found (Plate Vʙ), and several falls together here have a total height of about 30 m. forming a complete obstruction to migratory fish. Below this fall, the river flows almost directly westward through arable pasture-land and occasional patches of woodland—mostly deciduous. Several important tributaries enter the main river along this stretch, notably the Gonachan, Balglass and Maucher burns on the left bank, and the Balgair Burn on the right bank (Fig. 2). The river bed here is mostly stony, though there are some stretches of bare rock and often large areas of coarse gravel, much of which lies uncovered at low water levels. Typically, stretches of riffle and pool alternate with one another and even in the latter the current is strong.

Below the Pot of Gartness the character of the river changes somewhat: the greater part of its bed here consists of gravel and small stones—except in some places just below this waterfall where the bare sandstone is exposed. Several important tributaries enter in this stretch, notably the Blane Water and Catter Burn on the left bank and the Altquhur Burn on the right. The first of these is by far the largest and most important tributary entering the main river and, as is shown below, has an important influence on the river below its outfall.

South-west of Drymen the river enters its flood-plain proper and meanders widely before entering Loch Lomond (Fig. 1). Here, the lower reaches of the River Endrick form the county boundary between Stirlingshire to the north and Dunbartonshire to the south. The banks of the river in this stretch are steep and the river bed consists mostly of fine sand, with very little in the way of organic silt, except at the edge. Near the mouth, however, the current slows sufficiently to allow the finer silts to settle out, and these, together with many dead leaves and sand, form the substrate. Most of the land surrounding the lower reaches is permanent pasture, being too liable to flooding to be cultivated further. Only a few tributaries join the river here, the most important being the Burn of Mar which enters on the right bank a short distance above the mouth. Several ox-bow lakes in the adjacent pastureland afford evidence of past changes in the course of the river.

Land Use

The population of the Endrick valley as a whole and the direct effects of local water usage on the river are considered in full elsewhere (Maitland, 1962b, and below). Man's influence on the river is concerned not only with his use of water but also with the secondary effects of his other activities, notably the use to which the land of the river valley is put.

The River Endrick provided power for the development of several mills in its valley during the 18th and 19th centuries; there were several meal mills, two cotton mills and at least one woollen mill during this period. For many of these the flow of the River Endrick proved too irregular, and several power reservoirs were constructed in the upland areas. Though all the mills are now closed—the last one as recently as 1943—these reservoirs remain, and presumably will have an enriching effect on the stretches of the river below them similar to that described by Müller (1955) and discussed further below.

Farming is the main occupation of the people throughout the valley. Mixed farming predominates, though some farmers tend to specialize in dairying or sheep farming according to their land. Hunter (1960) divides the land in the upper part of the valley into three types: (i) The fertile valley bottom and the lower hill slopes below 100 m., where the land is mostly used for crops. (ii) The middle hill slopes between 100 and 300 m., which form first-class hill grazing. (iii) The land above 300 m., which represents poor-quality hill grazing. This same scheme of classification is true for the lower part of the Endrick valley, except for the extreme lower reaches where flooding makes cultivation of crops difficult.

Since 1936, the Forestry Commission have been planting the 1200 hectares of land which they own in the upper valley near

Carron Reservoir; there are also similar areas of forest planted near Drymen. The main species which have been grown so far are Norway and Sitka Spruce (*Picea abies* (L.) and *P. sitchensis* (Bong.)), with some Scots Pine (*Pinus sylvestris* L.) and Larch (*Larix decidua* Mill.). There is a good deal of private woodland scattered over the lower slopes of the Endrick valley below the Loup of Fintry, Oak (*Quercus robor* L.) being the dominant species here.

There are few industries in the area: two of the most important are service ones—the hospital at Killearn and the 'bus station at Balfron. The other industries are minor ones—several small saw mills, a distillery and a sand and gravel works, whilst the basalts of the Campsie Fells and the Kilpatrick Hills are quarried to provide road metal.

The largest villages in the area—Balfron (pop. 1250), Drymen (pop. 750), Killearn (pop. 745) and Strathblane (pop. 670) are all developing along the same lines. There has been a gradual movement of people into these villages from the surrounding countryside, whilst the villages themselves are tending to develop as dormitory areas for the city of Glasgow. This trend seems likely to continue and will probably be the only change in the area for many years (see below), for there is little other development planned at present (Hunter, 1960).

Climate

The climate of the Endrick valley is fairly typical of much of the West of Scotland, being in general rather cool and wet (Halstead, 1958). Average air temperatures vary from just below freezing point in winter to about 25°C. in summer (see Fig. 8), though altitude has an obvious effect on this, a subject which is further discussed below in connection with water temperatures in the river. The average annual rainfall is usually about 130 cm. on the lower ground and 150 cm. or more in the hills (Fig. 7); in the winter of each year some of this normally falls as snow.

Flora

No attempt was made to survey the flora of the River Endrick in detail. Only occasionally were Algae examined, and the specific identity of only one moss—*Fontinalis antipyretica* (L.)—was established. This species is found in all parts of the river, but especially

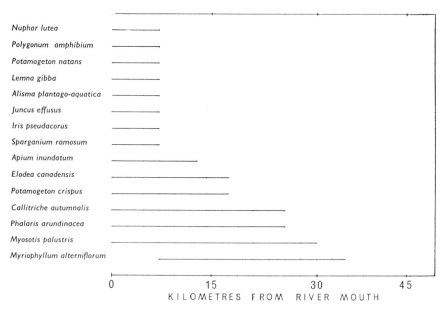

Nuphar lutea

Polygonum amphibium

Potamogeton natans

Lemna gibba

Alisma plantago-aquatica

Juncus effusus

Iris pseudacorus

Sparganium ramosum

Apium inundatum

Elodea canadensis

Potamogeton crispus

Callitriche autumnalis

Phalaris arundinacea

Myosotis palustris

Myriophyllum alterniflorum

0   15   30   45
KILOMETRES FROM RIVER MOUTH

Fig. 3.—The distribution of common species of Angiosperm in the River Endrick

in the middle reaches. Of the higher plants (Angiosperms), those species common in the river were collected and identified and are included in Fig. 3. This figure also includes emergent species common along the river banks, which, though not true hydrophytes, are at least partly submerged for some period of the year. The only tree to occur regularly along the river bank is the Alder—*Alnus glutinosa* (L.).

It can be seen from Fig. 3 that there are relatively few common species of macrophyte in the River Endrick. Those which do occur show, for the most part, the type of transition from mouth to source which is similar to that described below for the fauna. The differences from one place to another are evidently due to the nature of the flow at these points—the speed of the current (particularly during summer when all these species make most of their growth) and the nature of the substrate (notably its particle size and degree of stability) being the most important inter-related factors (Butcher, 1933).

The extreme lower reaches have a typical and fairly rich macrophytic community; none of the species concerned, however, grows in mid-stream, presumably because of the instability of the substrate here. In the more stable parts of the river bed near both banks *Apium inundatum* (L.), *Elodea canadensis* (Michx.), and *Potamogeton crispus* (L.) are common, whilst *Callitriche autumnalis* (L.) also occurs in places. The most typical plants of this stretch are those which possess floating leaves, *Nuphar lutea* (L.), *Polygonum amphibium* (L.), *Potamogeton natans* (L.), and *Lemna gibba* (L.) all being found here. On stable uneroded banks *Myosotis palustris* (L.), *Alisma plantago-aquatica* (L.), *Juncus effusus* (L.), *Iris pseudacorus* (L.), *Sparganium ramosum* (Huds.), and *Phalaris arundinacea* (L.) are all common. The most characteristic community is one in which the dominant species are *Juncus effusus*, *Phalaris arundinacea* and *Potamogeton natans*. These always show a well-defined zonation (Plate IA) in that order from the river bank into deeper water.

The remaining parts of the lower reaches have a much poorer macrophytic community in which no floating-leaved forms are found. Several submerged species are common, however, notably *Myriophyllum alterniflorum* (D. C.), *Callitriche autumnalis* (L.), *Apium inundatum* (L.), *Elodea canadensis* (Michx.), and *Potamogeton crispus* (L.). In places these may grow thickly on all parts of the river bed, and the particular abundance of some species (e.g. *E. canadensis* and *P. crispus*) is apparently associated with mild organic sewage (Maitland, 1962b). There is little in the way of marginal vegetation here, though occasionally clumps of *Myosotis palustris* and *Phalaris arundinacea* may occur.

In the middle reaches only two species of aquatic Angiosperm are found—*Myriophyllum alterniflorum* and *Callitriche autumnalis*. Both are commoner in the lower parts of this stretch, but even here *C.*

autumnalis is never abundant. Emergent marginal vegetation is rare and the banks are often eroded and steep or composed of unstable gravel deposit. In the latter, *Mimulus guttatus* (D. C.), and *Myosotis palustris* (L.), are found in summer, whilst *M. palustris* and *Phalaris arundinacea* occur occasionally as emergents at the edges of some of the larger pools in the river.

In the upper reaches of the river there are no truly aquatic species of Angiosperm to be found. *Fontinalis antipyretica* and other mosses occur frequently, however, and often cover many of the stable boulders in this part of the river (Plate IIIA). These mosses are of great importance as a source of food and shelter to many invertebrates in this otherwise rather barren stretch. The only marginal vegetation found here is near the source where the river rises in a marsh of *Juncus effusus* (Plate IIIB).

Plate Iᴀ.—The lower reaches of the River Endrick at station 2 (Woodend) looking downstream in summer, showing the thick weed growth which becomes established near the edge here at this time. Note the well-defined zonation of this emergent vegetation. It is probable that much of the summer fauna of the unstable sandy substrate in mid-stream here (station A in the quantitative studies) is recruited from this more stable weedy habitat. Pike, Perch and Roach are the most common fish species found in this part of the river

Plate Iʙ.—The middle reaches of the River Endrick at station 5 (Drumtian) looking downstream during winter. The current here is fast and the river is broad and shallow. The stony substrate in mid-stream in this stretch was one of the habitats chosen for quantitative study, as described in the text (station B)—The common fish species in this part of the river are Salmon, Trout, Minnows, Stone Loach and Three-spined Sticklebacks

Plate IIA.—The middle reaches of the River Endrick at station 7 (Dalfoil) looking downstream in winter. The river here is broad and shallow, the current is fast and the substrate rocky. The only aquatic plants found are mosses, whilst the common fish species are Salmon and Trout

Plate IIB.—The River Endrick at station 9 (Fintry) looking upstream in winter. This stretch is immediately below the Loup of Fintry (Plate VB); the current is swift and the substrate consists for the most part of bare rock and large boulders. Salmon and Trout are the most common fish occurring here

II. The Invertebrate Fauna

The establishment of a reliable check-list of the species of invertebrates found in the River Endrick was felt to be an essential part of any basic ecological study, and one which would obviously prove most useful in connection with other work on the fauna of the river. In conjunction with an inquiry of this type it was also considered desirable to find not only what species are in fact present in the river, but also how they are distributed. Ideally, such distribution should be studied both in time and space, but because of the amount of work involved it was found necessary to limit the study to an analysis of their distribution in space, and in particular their distribution in the main river from mouth to source. Some idea of the seasonal variation at each station was assessed by taking collections there in three different months of the year (see below). Many collections were also taken on selected tributaries, but these are not dealt with in full in the present account.

Methods

Twelve stations were chosen on the main river for sampling the invertebrate fauna; these included all the important environments found in the river from mouth to source. The samples of bottom fauna taken were not strictly quantitative, for such methods are very time-consuming and the apparatus necessary varies from one habitat to another (see Maitland, 1964a). It was decided instead to follow the method adopted by Macan (1957b) and Hynes (1961), and take comparable collections with a normal handnet for a standard period of time. All the collections made for the present study were with a circular handnet 40 cm. in diameter for a period of 10 minutes, using whatever method of collecting seemed to be most suitable for the habitat in question. The mesh used had 16 threads per cm. Each collection was placed individually in a plastic bag with a label, and

5 per cent formalin was added. Sorting was carried out later in the laboratory and the animals found were counted and identified.

Though a coarse mesh of the type used here is known to let through many of the smaller invertebrates (see below), it does retain the larger specimens of all groups except Protozoa, Rotifera and Nematoda. Accordingly, these groups are not considered in the present account, and as the main purpose of the collections was not to analyze the invertebrate populations as a whole, but merely to discover the species present, the mesh used was considered satisfactory. Moreover, from the point of view of identification, it is only the larger individuals of most groups which can be accurately named to species.

The twelve stations selected were chosen more or less at random along the length of the river, though care was taken not to site any where the fauna might be influenced by unnatural factors—e.g. near a sewage works or a ford. The stations were mostly about 3 to 5 km. apart, and each was given a code number as well as being named according to a nearby landmark (Fig. 2). At each station the river was examined carefully and the major habitats were selected for sampling. There were usually about two or three important habitats at each station, though at two places (Drumtian and Balfron) only one habitat was common, whilst at another (Drymen), seven habitats were considered to be of importance. Three series of collections were taken at all these stations—the first in October, 1959; the second in February, 1960; and the third in June, 1961. The individual collections in each series were taken as close together in time as possible, usually all within one week.

In addition to these three series, collections of the adults of some groups of insects (Trichoptera, Diptera, etc.) were made at all stations during the summer of 1961. Certain collections were also made to obtain larvae which were taken to the laboratory and reared to the adult stage. For this purpose small trays of the type described by Hynes (1941) were used, and these proved successful for most groups except Orthocladiinae, many species of which proved extremely difficult to rear. Other special collections were made at each station for certain aquatic species which might be common there but which would not be taken by normal methods, e.g. *Velia caprai*, *Gerris lateralis*, *Anodonta anatina*, etc.

The stations selected on the main river and the habitats examined at each are as follows:— (1) MOUTH. The greatest depth here is about 3 m. whilst the river is some 40 m. across. Two habitats were examined: (a) Silt in mid-stream; (b) Thick weed growth (partly emergent) in soft silt at the edge. (2) WOODEND. Here the maximum depth is about 2 m., and the river is some 35 m. in width (Plate VA). The two habitats examined were (a) Sand in mid-stream —this site was also studied quantitatively (station A) and is described more fully below—(b) Thick weed growth (partly emergent) in soft silt at the edge (Plate IA). (3) DRYMEN. The river here has a greatest depth of about 1·5 m. and is approximately 25 m. in width. Many different habitats are found in this stretch, due to the transitional nature of this part of the river (see below) and seven were examined: (a) *Myriophyllum* growing among clean gravel in mid-stream; (b) Coarse gravel in riffle; (c) Silted gravel at the edge of the river; (d) Sand and fine silt, also at the edge; (e) *Elodea* growing in soft silt; (f) Silted stones at the edge; (g) Stones in riffle. (4) DALNAIR. The greatest depth here is about 1 m., and the river is some 20 m. wide. Four habitats were examined: (a) Stones in riffle; (b) Silted gravel at the edge; (c) *Potamogeton* growing in silted gravel; (d) Silted stones at the edge of the river. (5) DRUMTIAN. The maximum depth at this station is about 80 cm., and the river is some 20 m. in width (Plate IB). Only one habitat is common here: (a) Stones in riffle (Plate IB). This site was also studied quantitatively (station B) and is described fully below. (6) BALFRON. Here the river is about 60 cm. deep and some 18 m. in width. One habitat only was examined: (a) Stones in riffle. (7) DALFOIL. The greatest depth here is about 50 cm. and the river is approximately 15 m. across (Plate IIA). Two habitats were examined: (a) Stones in riffle; (b) Stones in pool. (8) CULCREUCH. The maximum depth here is some 40 cm. and the river is about 10 m. in width. Three habitats were examined: (a) Stones in riffle; (b) Stones in pool; (c) *Fontinalis* growing on stones. (9) FINTRY. The greatest depth at this station is approximately 40 cm. and the river is about 10 m. in width (Plate IIB). Three habitats were examined here: (a) Stones in riffle; (b) Stones in pool; (c) *Fontinalis* growing on stones. (10) CRINGATE. Here the deepest water measures about 30 cm. and the river is some 6 m. in width (see

Plate 2 in Maitland, 1962*b*). Two habitats were examined: (a)
Boulders in riffle; (b) Moss growing on boulders. (11) BURNFOOT.
The greatest depth at this station is about 30 cm. and the river is some
2 m. wide (Plate IIIA). Three habitats were examined: (a) Boulders
in riffle; (b) Stones in pool; (c) Moss growing on solid rock. (12)
SOURCE. The maximum depth here is about 20 cm. and the river is
less than 1 m. in width (Plate IIIB). Two habitats were examined:
(a) Gravel and peat in riffle; (b) Moss growing over gravel and peat.

Further details about these stations can be seen in Figs. 1, 2, 20,
21 and 22.

Invertebrata

The general results of the survey described above are given in
Table 1, where the percentage composition of each collection has
been calculated and the results summed for each station—thus giving
some idea of the average composition of the fauna at that station.
As some groups (notably Diptera) could not always be fully identified,
the total number of species recorded at each station is almost certainly
an underestimation. All those species which have been recorded
from the River Endrick to date are now discussed further in the
systematic section below; the distribution of the species included in
Fig. 4 has been given on a standard basis of the numbers collected
in twenty minutes at each station in February, June and October
(i.e. a total of one hour's collecting). This gives some idea of the
numbers found at each place, as is further discussed below.

Porifera—Demospongiae

Only one species of this group has been found in the river, namely
Ephydatia fluviatilis (L.), which is common only in the lower reaches,
though it does extend upstream as far as the sewage effluent at Balfron
(Fig. 18). The largest growths of this species occur under stable
stones where the current is fast enough to prevent much settlement
of silt, but well-developed colonies are also found on the upper
surfaces of stable stones in places where the light intensity is never
great—e.g. below Drymen Bridge. Both Old (1932) and Berg (1948)
have noted this reaction to decreased light intensity. Steusloff (1938)

has shown that the most favourable conditions for this species are large stones in running water which is rich in suspended matter and which may even be slightly polluted. The distribution of *E. fluviatilis* in the River Endrick agrees with these observations—being limited in a downstream direction by the lack of suitable substrate and in an upstream direction by insufficient suspended matter in the water. Where large growths of this species occur, several invertebrates can be found burrowing among its tissues; notable among such animals are the larvae of *Sysira fuscata, Athripsodes nigronervosa* and *Endochironomus rufipes*.

Coelenterata—Hydrozoa

One species only of this group has been found in the River Endrick.

Hydra vulgaris (Pallas). This species occurs in most of the lower reaches of the River Endrick, and may be abundant in some habitats during the summer months. Large numbers are found attached to any substrate which is relatively stable—weed, rock and even algae growing over sand (e.g. at station 2, Woodend). It can maintain itself in strong currents, as the large numbers found on stones at station 5 (Drumtian) have shown.

Platyhelminthes—Turbellaria

It was not possible to identify accurately the few Rhabdocoela which were collected during the present survey, and only Tricladida are considered here. These are rarely abundant in the River Endrick, though they do occur in most parts of the river except the extreme upper reaches (Fig. 4A). Six species have been identified so far.

Dendrocoelum lacteum (Müller) is restricted to the lower reaches, where it is common, but never abundant, under stable silted boulders at the edge of the river.

Dugesia lugubris (Schmidt) is found only in the lower reaches, where it is common under silted stones and among suitable weed growth (e.g. the undersurface of *Nuphar* leaves) where the current is slow.

Polycelis tenuis (Ijima) also occurs only in the lower reaches, where

Table 1.—Percentage composition of the invertebrate fauna (a) and the number of species recorded (b) at stations 1 to 12 in the River Endrick

Fauna		1	2	3	4	5	6	7	8	9	10	11	12
Porifera	a	—	—	+	+	+	—	—	—	—	—	—	—
	b	—	—	1	1	1	—	—	—	—	—	—	—
Coelenterata	a	0·1	0·1	0·2	0·1	0·1	—	—	—	—	—	—	—
	b	1	1	1	1	1	—	—	—	—	—	—	—
Platyhelminthes	a	0·6	1·6	0·2	0·1	0·1	0·1	0·1	0·1	0·3	1·9	—	—
	b	2	3	4	4	2	2	1	1	2	2	—	—
Oligochaeta	a	24·6	25·7	8·9	33·5	7·8	11·6	1·9	0·8	0·5	0·8	0·9	7·5
	b	13	15	14	10	12	8	8	5	6	4	3	2
Hirudinea	a	0·5	0·1	0·2	5·9	0·2	0·1	0·1	—	—	—	—	—
	b	3	4	5	7	4	1	1	—	—	—	—	—
Crustacea	a	11·0	14·6	8·3	2·7	0·7	1·0	0·7	0·3	0·2	1·1	·	—
	b	15	15	11	6	4	2	2	1	1	2		—
Ephemeroptera	a	3·2	13·9	8·0	7·0	24·0	22·1	10·9	9·5	14·8	23·2	5·3	13·0
	b	7	8	12	10	9	9	11	13	12	12	10	8
Plecoptera	a	0·1	0·3	2·0	0·4	3·8	12·1	5·3	10·5	23·8	38·4	38·1	45·3
	b	1	3	15	9	12	10	13	12	14	10	12	11

Odonata	a	—	—	—	—	—	—	—	—	—	0·1	1·2	0·4
	b	—	—	—	—	—	—	—	—	—	1	3	3
Hemiptera	a	+	+	+	+	+	+	+	+	0·1	5·2	5·3	13·4
	b	2	1	1	1	1	1	1	1	2	4	8	9
Neuroptera	a	0·1	—	—	—	0·1	—	—	—	—	0·1	0·1	0·1
	b	1	—	—	—	1	—	—	—	—	1	1	1
Trichoptera	a	6·6	12·4	10·5	21·7	26·6	22·0	4·0	3·1	0·4	1·3	2·7	1·6
	b	6	10	11	13	15	14	10	10	14	13	5	6
Lepidoptera	a	—	—	—	—	—	—	—	—	—	—	0·1	0·1
	b	—	—	—	—	—	—	—	—	—	—	1	1
Diptera	a	19·9	33·9	20·2	30·6	36·7	36·9	29·3	38·5	35·4	48·7	26·1	31·9
	b	15	16	14	18	24	20	21	17	23	27	21	19
Coleoptera	a	7·2	4·2	3·3	4·6	6·7	8·7	13·8	14·5	8·1	7·6	0·9	0·5
	b	8	9	9	9	11	6	8	9	10	15	9	8
Hydracarina	a	0·1	0·1	0·2	0·2	0·7	1·0	5·4	0·8	1·4	1·2	1·7	0·1
	b	2	2	3	7	8	5	5	4	6	11	4	7
Mollusca	a	0·3	5·1	0·4	3·3	8·0	12·4	0·5	6·4	4·9	8·0	5·6	11·8
	b	1	1	1	2	2	2	2	3	8	9	12	9
Ectoprocta	a	—	—	—	—	+	—	—	—	+	+	+	+
	b	—	—	—	—	1	—	—	—	1	1	1	1
Number of Species		56	64	69	85	95	84	79	89	112	145	114	106

it is very common on most types of substrate in still water, generally where silting has taken place.

Polycelis nigra (Müller). The distribution of this species is similar to that of *P. tenuis*, but the latter is always the more common.

The distribution of the last four species in various types of water has been studied by Reynoldson (1958), who found that they are all

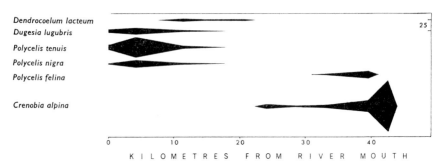

Fig. 4A.—The distribution of common Tricladida in the River Endrick

common only in rich waters with a high calcium content. Their distribution in the River Endrick agrees in general with this finding —though the stability of the substrate and its degree of silting are also of importance.

Polycelis felina (Dalyell) is found only in the upper reaches of the river, though never so far upstream as the source. This species, which is never abundant, is most common under stable boulders.

Crenobia alpina (Dana) occurs in the middle and upper reaches of the river, though it too is not found near the source. It usually occurs under stable boulders and among moss, and in places may be abundant.

The habitat of *P. felina* and *C. alpina* has been discussed by Reynoldson (1953), who pointed out that whilst both are undoubtedly stenothermic, they may also be favourably influenced by waters of high calcium content. Their distribution in the River Endrick agrees with this conclusion, and it would appear that both may be limited in a downstream direction by the higher temperatures found there, and in an upstream direction by the decreasing calcium content of the water.

Annelida—Oligochaeta

On account of taxonomic difficulties it was not possible to identify the Aelosomatidae and Enchytraeidae found in the River Endrick during the present study. Neither family was ever common. As a group, the Oligochaeta are found in all parts of the river, but they are clearly much more abundant both in density and numbers of species in the lower reaches (Fig. 4B). This abundance is possibly attributable to the larger amounts of silt present in all habitats in the lower reaches of the river, on which many of these animals depend for their food; this supposition is strengthened by the fact that the only part of the upper river where Oligochaeta are common is near the source, where the substrate is soft and silted by virtue of the peat deposits found there (Plate IIIB). Some twenty species have been recorded from the river so far.

Chaetogaster diaphanus (Gruithuisen) occurs only in the lower reaches of the river, especially the slow-flowing stretches between the mouth and Drymen. Here it is abundant during summer at the edge of the river among weed and fine silt, and it may also occur in mid-stream when the substrate there stabilizes (see the quantitative studies below). This is the only species of *Chaetogaster* recorded from Loch Lomond by Weerekoon (1956) who noted that it is very common there in some places.

Chaetogaster cristallinus (Vejdovski) is not uncommon among silted gravel in both middle and lower reaches of the river, and it too appears to be most abundant during summer.

Chaetogaster limnaei (von Baer) occurs only in the lower reaches of the river where, as is the normal habit of this species (Sperber, 1950), it is commensal on *Ancylus fluviatilis*, *Physa fontinalis* and *Lymnaea pereger*.

Uncinais uncinata (Ørsted) also occurs only in the lower reaches, where it is common, but never abundant among sand and silt.

Ophidonais serpentina (Müller). The distribution of this species is similar to that of *C. diaphanus*, it being found only in the lower reaches of the river, where it may be abundant during summer among weed growing in silt in shallow water.

Nais pseudobtusa (Piguet) is found in all parts of the river except

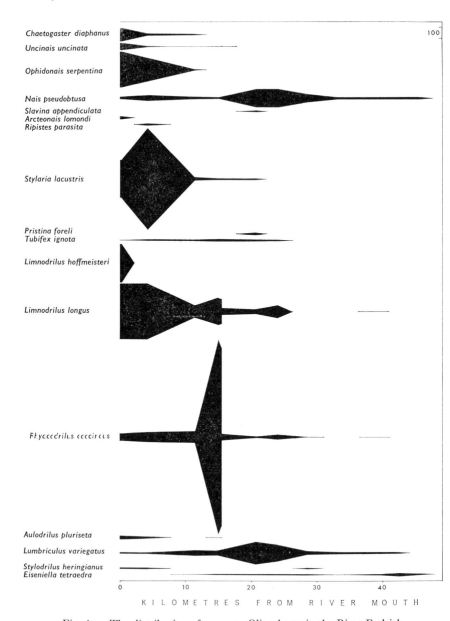

Fig. 4B.—The distribution of common Oligochaeta in the River Endrick

the extreme upper reaches. It is common in a variety of habitats during summer, especially algae growing on stones, although it never appears to be abundant. This species has only recently been confirmed for Britain by Brinkhurst (1962).

Slavina appendiculata (d'Udekem), though an uncommon species in the river, has been found occasionally in the lower reaches among weed growing in silt.

Arcteonais lomondi (Martin) occurs only in the extreme lower reaches of the river, just above the mouth, where it is common among fine silt—both at the edge and in mid-stream (Plate IVA). This part of the river is characterized by the presence of such fine silts, and the occurrence of this species here agrees with the finding of Weerekoon (1956) that, in Loch Lomond, *A. lomondi* is much commoner on mud than on sand.

Ripistes parasita (Schmidt) is an uncommon species, found only in the lower reaches. Here, specimens have been collected occasionally among weed growing in silt at the edge of the river near station 2 (Woodend).

Stylaria lacustris (L.) is common in the lower part of the river, being abundant during the summer months among weed growing in silt. Weerekoon (1956) also noted a pronounced maximum in summer for a population of this species in Loch Lomond.

Dero digitata (Müller) did not occur in any of the regular collections taken in the main river, but during collections made in connection with pollution studies (Maitland, 1962*b*) it was found to be very common among fine silt and sewage fungus below the Balfron sewage effluent. (Other Oligochaeta abundant here were *Nais pseudobtusa* and *Rhyacodrilus coccineus*—see Table 19).

Pristina foreli (Piguet) occurs in the lower part of the river, where it was often found during summer among silted gravel. This species is easily overlooked on account of its small size, and it has only recently been recorded as occurring in Britain by Brinkhurst (1963).

Tubifex ignota (Stolc) is found only in the lower reaches of the river where it is not uncommon among sand and fine silt. It seldom, however, occurs in large numbers here.

Limnodrilus hoffmeisteri (Claparède) also occurs only in the lower reaches of the river. It seems to be favoured by fine silts, for it has only been found in abundance in the stretches just above the mouth where such deposits occur. Here, large numbers have been collected, both at the edge of the river and in mid-stream.

Limnodrilus longus (Bretscher) is a very common species in the lower part of the river. Though most abundant among sand, it is also common in silted gravel, and its numbers are greatly increased by mild organic pollution.

Peloscolex ferox (Eisen) is an uncommon species in the river, having been found only occasionally, in small numbers, among silt in the middle and lower reaches.

The rarity of this species in the River Endrick is somewhat unusual in view of the fact that Weerekoon (1956) found it to be abundant in Loch Lomond. Even more surprising perhaps is the fact that *Tubifex tubifex* (Müller)—which is also abundant in Loch Lomond—has not yet been recorded from the River Endrick, though it is known to occur commonly in rivers elsewhere in Great Britain (Brinkhurst, 1960).

Rhyacodrilus coccineus (Vejdovski) occurs in both the middle and the lower reaches of the river, being most common among silted gravel, though it also occurs in large numbers among sand and fine silt. Its abundance in the River Endrick is notably affected by mild organic pollution, and the large population of this species found at station 4 (Dalnair) is due to slight pollution from the Blane Water—which enters the main river just above this point (Fig. 2). It is also abundant in the silt and sewage fungus found below sewage effluents in the Endrick valley.

Aulodrilus pluriseta (Piguet) occurs only in the lower reaches of the river, where it is found commonly among sand and finer silts in mid-stream. It is never an abundant species.

Lumbriculus variegatus (Müller) occurs in all parts of the river except the extreme upper reaches near the source. It is found in a variety of habitats ranging from fine silt to coarse gravel under stones, but appears to be most abundant among silted gravel in the lower reaches of the river.

Stylodrilus heringianus (Claparède) occurs only in the lower reaches of the River Endrick, where it is common among sand and gravel in mid-stream.

Eiseniella tetraedra (Savigny) alone of the Oligochaeta found in the River Endrick is more common in the upper reaches than elsewhere. It does, however, occur in most parts of the river except the extreme lower reaches. It is found among coarse gravel and stones and appears to be particularly abundant under moss growing on boulders in the upper reaches.

Annelida—Hirudinea

As a group, these are restricted to the lower reaches of the River Endrick, rarely making up a large part of the invertebrate population there. The only exception to this is found at such places as station 4 (Dalnair), where mild pollution from the Blane Water affects the

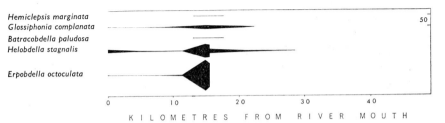

Fig. 4c.—The distribution of common Hirudinea in the River Endrick

numbers of leeches very favourably. Mann (1955) has shown that many of the British species of Hirudinea are most abundant in waters with a high calcium content; the results from the present study are in agreement with this (Fig. 4c), for only in the lower reaches of the River Endrick does the calcium content of the water ever become much greater than his soft category (0–17 mg./l. $CaCO_3$). Bennike (1943) and Mann (1955) both found that *Glossiphonia complanata*, *Helobdella stagnalis* and *Erpobdella octoculata* are the only European species of leech which are ever abundant in running water, and certainly these three are the only common ones in the River Endrick, from which, however, nine species of Hirudinea have been recorded altogether.

Theromyzon tessulatum (Müller) is very uncommon in the River Endrick, and only occasionally have isolated specimens been found attached to stones and to weed in the lower reaches.

Hemiclepsis marginata (Müller). This is a rare leech in Scotland, and its occurrence in the River Endrick has been reported in full elsewhere (Maitland, 1963). It has been found attached to the undersurfaces of stones in the lower reaches of the river where it is, however, uncommon.

Glossiphonia complanata (L.) is common in the lower half of the river, where it may be found attached to the undersurfaces of stones, even where the current is strong. This species may also occur among suitable plant growths (e.g. *Nuphar*) which offer it a firm substrate. It is never an abundant species.

Glossiphonia heteroclita (L.) has never been recorded from the main river. It has been found, however, in small numbers underneath stones in shallow water at the outflow from Wattie's Dam, a small reservoir whose waters flow eventually into the River Endrick via the Blane Water.

Batracobdella paludosa (Carena). This species of leech appears to be a very rare one in Britain (from where it was recorded by Mann for the first time as recently as 1953) and elsewhere in Europe. Its occurrence in the River Endrick is reported in full elsewhere (Maitland, 1963). A very uncommon species in the river, it has only been found on one occasion, when five specimens were collected at station 4 (Dalnair) from the undersurfaces of stones in shallow water.

Helobdella stagnalis (L.) is common in the lower half of the river where it occurs in a variety of habitats ranging from stones in fast flowing water (e.g. at station 5, Drumtian) to fine silt where the current is very slow indeed (e.g. at station 1, Mouth). It appears to be most abundant under stones where slight silting occurs, and is very common in this habitat just below the sewage effluent from Killearn Hospital. Slack (1957c) has noted that this species occurs even on the fine silts of the profundal region of Loch Lomond, and it appears to be this versatility which enables *H. stagnalis* to be the most widely distributed leech in the Endrick system.

Erpobdella octoculata (L.) is found only in the lower reaches of the river, where it is common under stones both in fast current in midstream and at the edge where the current is slow and silting occurs. Large numbers of this species are associated with organic pollution from the Blane Water, the effect presumably being a secondary one due to the increased numbers of food animals (e.g. *Rhyacodrilus* and *Orthocladius*) present under such conditions (Maitland, 1962*b*). Bennike (1943) too has noted that this species is favoured by mild organic pollution.

Dina lineata (Müller) occurs only in the lower reaches of the river at station 4 (Dalnair), where several specimens were found attached to stones at the edge among *Myosotis*. This species has also been found in small numbers in two of the tributary streams—the Burn of Mar and the Blane Water—where it was collected from a similar habitat.

Haemopsis sanguisuga (L.) is a very uncommon species in the River Endrick and has never been found in the main river. Single specimens have, however, been collected from the Maucher Burn and the outflow from Wattie's Dam, both individuals being found attached to the undersurfaces of stones partly buried among silt in shallow water.

Arthropoda—Crustacea

With the exception of *Gammarus pulex*, this group is common only in the lower reaches of the River Endrick, and only here does it form a significant part of the invertebrate population (Fig. 4D). This restriction is probably due to the fact that most species are unable to maintain themselves against a strong current, and so it is only in the lower reaches, where the current is slow, that they can become established. Interstitial forms do occur in the middle reaches among the gravel there, but these are all small Harpacticoidea, none of which were identified in the present study because of taxonomic difficulties. Nineteen different species of Crustacea have been recorded from the river so far.

Cyclops fuscus (Jurine) occurs only in the lower reaches of the river, where it is common among algae growing over sand and silt in water more than one metre deep.

Cyclops agilis (Koch) is also found only in the lower reaches, being most abundant among weed growing in silt there.

Cyclops fimbriatus (Fischer). The distribution and occurrence of this species appear to be similar to those of *C. fuscus*, though the latter is much more common.

Cyclops vernalis (Fischer) is most common among fine silt and algae in the lower reaches of the river, though it also occurs among coarse gravel—even where a slight current is present.

Cyclops viridis (Jurine) occurs only in the lower reaches, but is common there in a variety of habitats, being most abundant among weed growing in silt. Weerekoon (1956) found it to be the commonest species of the genus in Loch Lomond, and it is probable that this is the case in the River Endrick also.

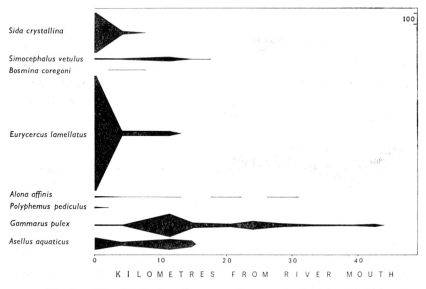

Fig. 4D.—The distribution of common Crustacea in the River Endrick

Cyclops albidus (Jurine) occurs only in the lower reaches of the river and never appears to be common. Several specimens were collected among bare silt in shallow water here during summer.

Herpetocypris reptans (Baird) is found only in the lower reaches of the river. This species is most common among weed growing in silt and at times it may be abundant in this habitat.

Sida crystallina (Müller) is also found only in the lower reaches, where it is very common during summer among thick weed growth.

Simocephalus vetulus (Müller) is one of the most common Cladocera in the lower reaches of the river, and may be abundant over bare silt and among weed growing in silt.

Bosmina coregoni (Baird) occurs only in the extreme lower reaches of the river, just above the mouth, where it is common during summer over bare silt and among weed growing in silt.

Eurycercus lamellatus (Müller). The distribution of this species is similar to that of *S. vetulus*, and during summer it is extremely abundant among weed growing in silt.

Alona affinis (Leydig) is found in both the lower and the middle reaches of the river, occurring much further upstream than any other species of Cladocera, and having been found in a variety of habitats. It is most common, however, among algae growing over sand and silt in the lower reaches (e.g. the substrate studied quantitatively at station A, Woodend). In the middle reaches it is found only among coarse, silted gravel.

Rhynchotalona rostrata (Koch) is a very uncommon species, and has been found only in the lower reaches among sand and fine silt in deep water.

Pleuroxus uncinatus (Baird.) The distribution and occurrence of this species are similar to those of *R. rostrata*, both being uncommon species.

Chydorus ovalis (Kurz) is found only in the lower reaches of the river, where during summer it is common but never abundant among weed growing in silt where the water is shallow.

Polyphemus pediculus (L.) is the only predatory member of the Cladocera found in the River Endrick, and like most of the rest of the group occurs only in the lower reaches. Here it is abundant during the summer months in still, shallow water at the edge of the river.

Bathynella natans (Vejdovski). The occurrence of this small interstitial crustacean (Plate IVB) in the River Endrick is the first record of this species in Scotland, and has been reported in full elsewhere (Maitland, 1962a). It has never been found in the main river and appears to be restricted to a single tributary—the Altquhur Burn—where it is not uncommon among the gravel beds which are a characteristic feature of this stream (Plate VIA).

Gammarus pulex (L.) is found in all parts of the river except the extreme upper reaches. It is most common, however, in the lower reaches and also in many of the tributaries; in places it may be abundant among *Myriophyllum* or under stones, in both slow- and fast-flowing water. Schumann (1928) and other workers have suggested that calcium may be a limiting factor in its distribution, though Macan and Mackereth (1957) note that if this is the case then the threshold must be considerably lower than was estimated by these workers, for they record this species in waters where the calcium content is as low as 2 mg./l. Data from the River Endrick would suggest that this may in fact be close to its tolerance limit, for no specimens have ever been found where the calcium content of the water is less than this value.

Asellus aquaticus (L.) is found only in the lower reaches of the river, where it is common in a variety of habitats, notably among silt, weed growing in silt, gravel, and stones where the current is slow. Weerekoon (1956) noted that in Loch Lomond this species prefers sandy substrates to silted ones, but in the River Endrick the opposite has been found to be the case, it being most abundant in habitats which are highly silted and absent from places where bare sand occurs. *A. aquaticus* is one of several species in the River Endrick which show an abrupt zonation upstream, for it is very common in the main river below the junction with the Blane Water but absent above. It is, however, common in the Blane Water for several kilometres above the main river (Fig. 2). The mild organic pollution occurring in the Blane Water (Maitland, 1962b) could be responsible for this unusual distribution and the subject is further discussed below.

Arthropoda—Insecta

Ephemeroptera

As a group these form an important part of the invertebrate population in all parts of the river, especially the middle and upper reaches (Fig. 4E). The ephemeropteran fauna of the River Endrick is rich in species as well as in numbers—twenty-one different species having been recorded so far—and these show a varied distribution within the river system.

Caenis horaria (L.) is a most uncommon species in the river and only two specimens have been found in the lower reaches among weed growing in silt at station 1 (Mouth). Weerekoon (1956) records *C. horaria* as being abundant in Loch Lomond; and it would appear

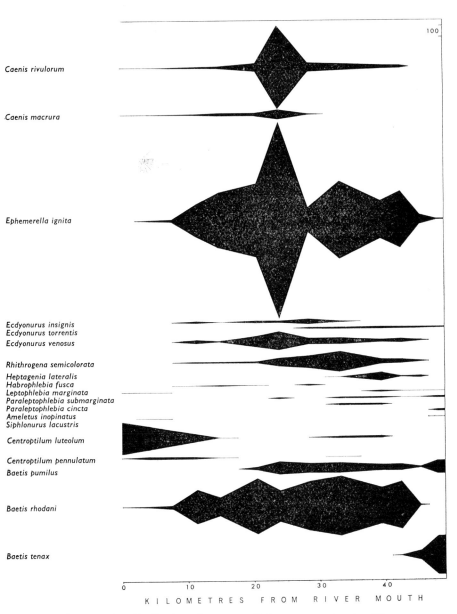

Fig. 4E.—The distribution of common Ephemeroptera in the River Endrick

that it is definitely a still-water form (cf. *Peloscolex ferox* above). Macan (1955) too records this species only from standing waters.

Caenis rivulorum (Eaton) is found in most parts of the river except the extreme upper reaches, having its optimum habitat in the middle reaches among gravel and stones, even where the current is strong. Macan (1955) says that this species can tolerate stronger currents than other members of the genus, and its distribution in the River Endrick certainly agrees with this statement.

Caenis macrura (Stephens) occurs only in the lower and middle reaches of the river, where its habitat is quite distinct from that of *C. rivulorum*, since it is common only where the current is slow and silting takes place, e.g. among bare silt or silted gravel at the edge of pools.

Ephemerella ignita (Poda) occurs in all parts of the river, though it is never common in the extreme upper or the extreme lower reaches. It is most common in the middle reaches of the river among weed and stones in current, and during the summer months is very abundant in such places. Nymphs are absent during the winter months (Maitland, 1964a), when the species is thought to be in the egg-stage (Macan, 1957a).

Ecdyonurus insignis (Eaton) is found in the middle reaches of the river and also that part of the lower reaches where the current is still strong enough to prevent the deposition of silt. It is common under stones, both in mid-stream, where the current is fast, and at the edge of the river, where the current is slower.

Ecdyonurus torrentis (Kimmins) occurs only in the middle and upper reaches of the river, where it occupies a similar habitat to that in which *E. insignis* is present further downstream. It is found right up to the source of the river, being common at station 12 (Source) among gravel and peat.

Ecdyonurus venosus (Fabricius) is found in all parts of the river, except the extreme upper and the extreme lower reaches. It appears to occupy a similar habitat to the other two species of this genus occurring in the river, and, except in the extreme upper reaches, is usually more abundant than either of these.

Rhithrogena semicolorata (Curtis). Macan (1961c) has pointed out that it is impossible to distinguish between the nymphs of *R. semi-*

colorata and those of *R. haarupi* (Esben-Petersen.) All the adults of this genus caught in the Endrick area, however, were identified as the former species: it is probable that this is the commonest, if not the only one, present in the river. Nymphs of *Rhithrogena* are found in all parts of the river except the extreme lower and the extreme upper reaches, being most abundant among stones in riffle (see Macan, 1960*a*).

Heptagenia lateralis (Curtis) occurs only in the upper reaches of the river, though it is not found right up to the source. Common among stones in riffle in this part of the river, it never appears to be an abundant species. Macan (1960*b*) has also found this species to be restricted to the upper reaches of rivers, relating this distribution to its temperature requirements during development.

Habrophlebia fusca (Curtis) is found only in the lower reaches of the river and is never abundant. It appears to be most common among silted weed where the current is present but rather slow. Macan (1961*c*) has recorded this species from similar habitats in English rivers.

Leptophlebia marginata (L.) occurs in the lower and middle reaches of the river, mostly where the current is slow and vegetation from the river bank hangs into the water. It is never an abundant species.

Paraleptophlebia submarginata (Stephens) is found in the middle and upper reaches of the river, where it is common among *Fontinalis* and other mosses in places where the current is weak. This species has also been found in abundance in several small tributaries flowing into the Blane Water, in which it occurred among dead *Juncus* stems hanging into the water from the surrounding marshy ground.

Paraleptophlebia cincta (Retzius) is found in the same sort of habitat as *P. submarginata*, but occurs only in the middle reaches of the river. It is never as common as the latter species.

Ameletus inopinatus (Eaton) is restricted to the extreme upper reaches of the river, being common at station 12 (Source) among moss, and in smaller numbers among peat and gravel in riffle here. *A. inopinatus* is a stenothermic species and is the only arctic-alpine ephemeropteran known to occur in Great Britain (Gledhill, 1959). This stenothermy is presumably responsible for its restriction to the upper reaches of the River Endrick.

Siphlonurus lacustris (Eaton) occurs in all parts of the river, though it is usually uncommon, only a few specimens having been found in general collections taken from the main river. It has been found commonly, however, among gravel and stones in still water at the edge of the river in the upper reaches, where little silting had taken place, and was noted to be abundant also in small pools in gravel beside the river in this area.

Centroptilum luteolum (Müller) is most common among weed growing in silt and on bare silt in the lower reaches of the river, where it is the only abundant ephemeropteran. This species also occurs in the middle reaches of the river, among weed in places where the current is slow.

Centroptilum pennulatum (Eaton) also occurs in the lower and middle reaches, where it occupies the same habitat as *C. luteolum*. It is far less common than that species, however.

Cloëon simile (Eaton) is very uncommon in the River Endrick, and only two specimens have been collected so far in the lower reaches, where they occurred among weed growing in silt.

Baetis pumilus (Burmeister) is found in the middle and upper reaches of the river, being common there among moss in current and also among stones in riffle. It is never an abundant species, however.

Baetis rhodani (Pictet) is the most common member of the Ephemeroptera found in the River Endrick, and occurs in all parts except the extreme upper and lower reaches. It is common on most substrates where the current is not so weak as to allow the deposition of silt, and is especially abundant among moss and stones in current in the middle reaches.

Baetis tenax (Eaton). Macan (1961c) states that he finds it impossible to distinguish between the nymphs of *B. vernus* Curtis and those of *B. tenax* Eaton. There appears to be some doubt, moreover, as to whether or not these are in fact distinct species, and for the purposes of the present account both are referred to *Baetis tenax* Eaton. In the River Endrick, nymphs of this species are confined to the upper reaches, and are abundant at station 12 (Source) among moss, and among gravel and peat in riffle. It appears to replace *B. rhodani* completely in this part of the river.

Plecoptera

The plecopteran fauna of the River Endrick is a rich one, some twenty species having been recorded so far. As a group they occur in all parts of the river from source to mouth, though their importance varies greatly from one part to another (Fig. 4F). In the lower reaches only one or two species occur, and these form but a small part of the invertebrate fauna as a whole. In the middle reaches there are many species, but these still form only a small part of the total invertebrate population; whilst in the upper reaches the number of species is high and the group forms a very important part of the invertebrate fauna here.

Taeniopteryx nebulosa (L.) occurs irregularly in all parts of the river and is never an abundant species. It has been taken in a variety of habitats, but appears to be most common among stones in riffle and *Myriophyllum* growing in gravel in the lower reaches.

Brachyptera risi (Morton) is most common among stones in riffle, but also occurs among *Myriophyllum* and *Fontinalis* in the lower and middle reaches of the river.

Protonemura meyeri (Pictet) occurs in the middle and upper reaches of the river, where it may at times be abundant among *Fontinalis* and other mosses.

Amphinemura standfussi (Ris) is a very uncommon species in the River Endrick, and has been found only in the upper reaches at station 12 (Source), where several specimens were collected among moss in shallow water.

Amphinemura sulcicollis (Stephens) has been found in all parts of the River Endrick except the extreme lower reaches. It is most common in the upper reaches, however, especially among stones in riffle and among moss. Hynes (1941) suggests that it is absent from lowland streams because of the high amount of silting found there; this may well account for its distribution in the River Endrick.

Nemoura avicularis (Morton) occurs in most parts of the river, but is common only in the upper reaches. It was found to be abundant at station 12 (Source) among moss growing over gravel and peat—and also among gravel and peat in riffle. Hynes (1941) considers this species to be favoured by silting conditions, and the silting due to

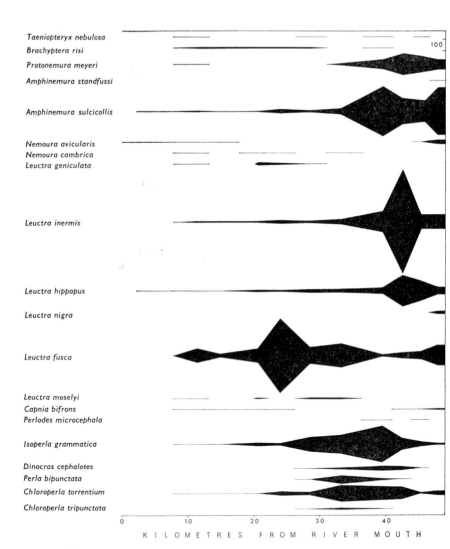

Fig. 4F.—The distribution of common Plecoptera in the River Endrick

peat near the source may well be an important factor in its distribution—as appears also to be the case with *Leuctra nigra* (see below).

Nemoura cambrica (Stephens) occurs in the middle reaches of the river and also in part of the lower reaches, though never in the stretches just above the mouth. It is most common among gravel and stones in riffle in the middle reaches, but is never abundant here. This species has, however, been taken in large numbers from among stones in riffle in some of the tributaries (e.g. Finnich Burn) which enter the middle and lower reaches of the river.

Leuctra geniculata (Stephens) is restricted to the middle reaches of the river, where it is common during summer among gravel and small stones. Lestage (1918) has suggested that the peculiar processes on the antennae of this species are concerned with burrowing in gravel, and it is certainly true that in the River Endrick it is found only where large areas of clean gravel are present.

Leuctra inermis (Kempny) occurs in all parts of the river except the extreme lower reaches, but it is most common in the upper reaches, where it may be abundant among stones in riffle and among moss during the winter months.

Leuctra hippopus (Kempny). The distribution and occurrence of this species are almost identical to that of *L. inermis*, and it is even more abundant in places than that species.

Leuctra nigra (Olivier) occurs only in the upper reaches of the river. It is very common at station 12 (Source) among gravel and peat in riffle, and it also occurs among moss here. Like *N. avicularis* its abundance in this part of the river may be partly due to the silting effect of the peat, for Hynes (1941) has noted that it is most abundant in silty localities.

Leuctra fusca (L.) is found during summer in all parts of the river except the extreme lower reaches, being most common among stones in riffle and among moss in the middle and upper reaches. It appears to be more tolerant of pollution than other Plecoptera, for it is the only species commonly found in the silted stretches below sewage effluents in the area (Maitland, 1962*b*).

Leuctra moselyi (Morton) occurs only in the middle reaches of the river where it is found among stones and gravel in riffle during summer. It appears to be a rather uncommon species, however.

Capnia bifrons (Newman) is found irregularly in all parts of the river except the extreme lower reaches. It is never very common, and occurs mostly among weed and detritus in places where the current is slow.

Perlodes microcephala (Pictet) occurs in the middle and upper reaches of the river, though never commonly. The few specimens which have been taken so far were found among stones in riffle and among moss.

Isoperla grammatica (Poda) is found in all parts of the river except the extreme lower reaches. Its optimum habitat seems to be among stones in riffle and among moss in parts of the upper reaches, where it is often abundant. It occurs right up to the source of the river at well over 400 m. above sea-level, though Hynes (1941) notes that it is never found in the Lake District above 300 m.

Dinocras cephalotes (Curtis). This large species is found in the middle and upper reaches of the river, though it does not extend right up to the source. It is most frequently found among stones in riffle and is quite common in some stretches.

Perla bipunctata (Pictet) is also found in the middle and upper reaches of the river, and it too is not found so far upstream as the source. This species, which is never abundant, is most common among stones in riffle.

Chloroperla torrentium (Pictet), though found in all parts of the river except the extreme lower reaches, is most common in the middle reaches, where at times it may be abundant among stones in riffle as well as among gravel and moss.

Chloroperla tripunctata (Scopoli). The distribution of this species is much more restricted than that of *C. torrentium*, for it is found only in the middle reaches of the river. Here, it occurs in small numbers among stones in riffle and among moss—always along with *C. torrentium*. Hynes (1952) has also noted that the range of habitat occupied by *C. torrentium* is much greater than that occupied by *C. tripunctata*, part of this difference being almost certainly due to the fact that *C. tripunctata* appears to take two years to complete its life cycle whilst that of *C. torrentium* is annual (Hynes, 1941).

Odonata

As a group, these have been found so far only in the lower reaches of the River Endrick, especially in the slow-flowing stretches just above the mouth. Here they form a very characteristic, but never large, part of the invertebrate fauna. Only four species are known to occur in the river.

Ischnura elegans (Van der Linden) is found in most parts of the lower reaches, and is common among weed growing in silt. It is the most abundant damselfly found in the area, and adults are very common among emergent vegetation at the edge of the river during summer.

Pyrrhosoma nymphula (Sulzer) is restricted to the extreme lower reaches of the river among weed growing in silt in shallow water. Adults are common at the edge here during the summer months.

Enallagma cyathigerum (Charpentier) too is found only in the lower reaches of the river among weed growing in silt, and its adults also are common in this area during summer.

Cordulegaster boltoni (Donovan). The nymphs of this large species have never been taken in the River Endrick, though they have been collected by the author in the Douglas Water, a stream flowing into the north-west side of Loch Lomond. Adults have been seen many times in the Strathblane area of the Endrick valley (Fig. 1), and it is almost certain that the species breeds in the river in some places. The nymphs are normally found in fairly fast-flowing water among silt and gravel in which they lie buried.

Hemiptera

Other than certain surface-dwelling species, this group are all confined to the lower reaches of the river (Fig. 4G). Though many of them are efficient swimmers, they appear to be unable to maintain themselves in a current; possibly this is the reason for their restriction to the slow-flowing lower reaches. In addition, many of them feed on superficial deposits of silt, and it is only in this part of the river that fine silt settles out to any extent. Thirteen species have been recorded from the River Endrick.

Velia caprai (Tamanini) occurs in all parts of the river except the extreme lower reaches. It is found on the surface of the water near the edge where the current is slow, and is especially common where there is emergent or overhanging vegetation. Nymphs are abundant in such places during the summer months.

Gerris lateralis (Schummel) has never been found in the main river. It occurs commonly, however, among thick growths of *Hippurus* in a small, slow-flowing tributary which runs into the Blane Water.

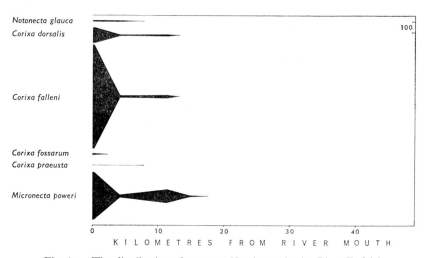

Fig. 4G.—The distribution of common Hemiptera in the River Endrick

Gerris costai (Herrich-Schaeffer) has been found only in the upper reaches of the river, where a single specimen was collected at station 12 (Source) on the surface of a small pool. Brinkhurst (1959) notes that this is a highland species confined to peat pools and stream margins; the present record agrees with this observation.

Gerris lacustris (L.) occurs only in the lower reaches of the river where there is emergent or floating-leaved vegetation. Here, it is common during the summer months. Brinkhurst (1959) notes that *G. lacustris* is found only in standing waters and never in rivers, but the present records show that this is not always the case.

Notonecta glauca (L.) is restricted to the extreme lower reaches of the river, where it is common, but never abundant, among weed growing in silt.

Nepa cinerea (L.) too occurs only in the extreme lower reaches of the main river, where it has been found occasionally among thick weed growth in shallow water. A single specimen was collected also in a stagnant ditch leading into the Blane Water. The species never appears to be an abundant one.

Corixa sahlbergi (Fieber) is a rare species in the River Endrick, one specimen only having been collected in the lower reaches at station 1 (Mouth) among weed growing in silt.

Corixa dorsalis (Leach) is found only in the lower reaches of the river, being very common there among weed growing in silt and also over bare silt in shallow water.

Corixa falleni (Fieber) is also abundant among weed growing in silt and over bare silt in the lower reaches of the river.

Macan (1954) groups *C. dorsalis* and *C. falleni* together as being typical of rivers, noting that the latter species is usually absent from lime-deficient waters. The present records agree with his findings, for these two species are undoubtedly the most abundant of their genus in the River Endrick.

Corixa distincta (Fieber) is an uncommon species, two specimens only having been collected in the lower reaches of the river at station 2 (Woodend) among weed growing in silt.

Corixa fossarum (Leach) occurs only in the extreme lower reaches of the river, where it is occasionally found among weed growing in silt in shallow water.

Corixa praeusta (Fieber) too occurs only in the extreme lower reaches, being common there (though never as abundant as either *C. dorsalis* or *C. falleni*) among weed growing in silt. Macan (1954) notes that this species is typical of waters which are highly productive or even slightly polluted, and that *C. dorsalis* and *C. falleni* are common in such places also.

Micronecta poweri (Douglas and Scott) occurs commonly in the River Endrick only in the lower reaches, though it extends further upstream than any of the other Hemiptera (apart from some surface-dwelling species), being still common at station 4 (Dalnair) among silted gravel. On one occasion a single specimen was found at the edge of the river as far upstream as station 6 (Balfron). It is most commonly found among weed growing in silt and over bare silt or silted gravel—always in shallow water—and under these conditions it may be very abundant.

Neuroptera

Members of this group are uncommon in the River Endrick, never making up a large proportion of the invertebrate fauna. Three species are known to occur.

Sialis lutaria (L.) is found only in the extreme lower reaches of the river, where the larvae are common, but never abundant, among soft silt at the edge. Adults are very common during summer among emergent vegetation and bushes at the edges of this part of the river.

Sialis fuliginosa (Pictet) has been found only in the extreme upper reaches of the river, where the larvae are common among gravel and peat in riffle. Kimmins (1944) has noted that *S. lutaria* occurs in ponds and slow-flowing silted rivers, whilst *S. fuliginosa* is confined to running water; the distribution of these two species in the River Endrick is in complete agreement with this observation.

Sisyra fuscata (Fabricius). A single adult of this species was collected among bushes overhanging the water in the lower reaches of the river at station 3 (Drymen). Larvae of *Sisyra* have also been collected at this station, where they were found burrowing into *Ephydatia fluviatilis*; they are never common, however.

Trichoptera

As a group these occur in all parts of the River Endrick, though they are most abundant in the middle and the upper reaches (Fig. 4H). In some habitats here they make up a large proportion of the invertebrate fauna (cf. Scott, 1958), and it is especially unfortunate in a group as important as this one that many of the larvae cannot yet be identified further than genus. This was to some extent overcome by rearing the larvae of certain species to the adult stage, and also by collecting adults by handnet at various points along the river. In spite of this, it was not possible to suggest the specific identity of any of the following genera which were collected as larvae from the river: *Halesus*, *Mystacides* and *Wormaldia*. Thirty-two species were recorded during the present survey of the River Endrick. King (1901) has also collected Trichoptera in the Endrick valley, and among the twelve species which he lists for the area *Limnephilus centralis* (Curtis), *Micropterna lateralis* (Stephens), *Crunoecia irrorata* (Curtis), *Athripsodes cinerea* (Curtis) and *Tinodes aureola* (Zetterstedt) have not been recorded by the present author.

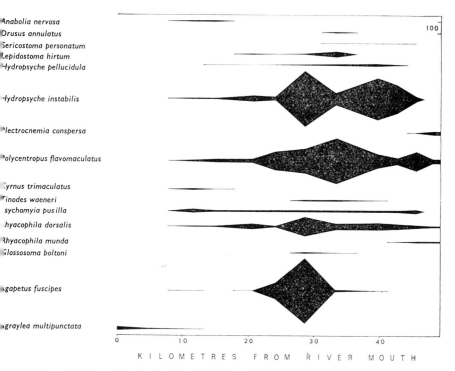

Fig. 4H.—The distribution of common Trichoptera in the River Endrick

Limnephilus vittatus (Fabricius). Larvae of *Limnephilus* are common only in the lower reaches of the river, though they do occur occasionally in parts of the middle and upper reaches. A single adult specimen of *L. vittatus* was collected among vegetation at the edge of the Maucher Burn (Fig. 2), and King (1901) has recorded this species near Strathblane.

Limnephilus extricatus (McLachlan). A single adult of this species was collected near station 5 (Drumtian) in the middle reaches of the river.

Limnephilus fuscicornis (Rambur). Adults of this species have been collected occasionally among emergent vegetation in the lower reaches of the river.

Anabolia nervosa (Curtis) too has been found only in the lower reaches of the river, where its larvae are common among clean sand and gravel in places where the current is slow.

Potamophylax stellatus (Curtis). Larvae of *Potamophylax* occur in all parts of the river, but are common only in stretches of the lower reaches, where they may be abundant under stones. In early summer a single stone here may have very many pupae attached to its undersurface. Adults collected at the edge of the river all proved to be *P. stellatus*, the larvae of which Philipson (1954) has shown to be unable to withstand very strong currents. This may account in part for it being common only in the lower reaches of the river.

Drusus annulatus (Stephens). Larvae of this species were found only in the middle reaches of the river at station 7 (Dalfoil) where several specimens were collected among stones in riffle. King (1901) records it from the Spout of Ballagan, a tributary of the Blane Water.

Sericostoma personatum (Spence) occurs only in the middle and upper reaches of the river, where it is common, but never abundant, among stones in riffle.

Goëra pilosa (Fabricius) occurs occasionally in the middle reaches of the river among stones and gravel in riffle.

Lepidostoma hirtum (Fabricius) is restricted to the middle reaches of the river, being most common among clean stones and gravel in shallow water, but also occurring among moss. In places it may be abundant.

Beraea maurus (Curtis). Adults of this species were collected at the edge of the Altquhur Burn, but no larvae have yet been found in the river.

Athripsodes nigronervosa (Retzius). Larvae of *Athripsodes* are found commonly in all parts of the river except the extreme upper and the extreme lower reaches. Adults of *A. nigronervosa* have been taken beside the lower reaches of the river at station 3 (Drymen) and also among emergent vegetation in the Blane Water. There is some evidence to suggest that the *Athripsodes* larvae which are found burrowing in colonies of *Ephydatia fluviatilis* in the lower reaches belong to this species.

Athripsodes aterrima (Stephens). Adults of this species were collected among vegetation near the edge of the river at several places in the lower reaches.

Athripsodes bilineata (L.). Adults of this species have been collected only among bushes overhanging the Altquhur Burn.

Hydropsyche pellucidula (Curtis) occurs in most parts of the river except the extreme upper and lower reaches. Its optimum habitat appears to be among stones in riffle, but it is never an abundant species.

Hydropsyche instabilis (Curtis) is much commoner than the previous species, although it has a similar distribution, being often abundant among stones in riffle. Adults are common under stones and among vegetation at the edge of the river during summer.

Badcock (1953*b*) has suggested that dense populations of *Hydropsyche* are usually correlated either with calcareous waters or with lake outflows: this does not appear to be true in the River Endrick, for both the above species are common in the upper reaches, where the calcium content of the water is low (less than 5 mg./l.), and into which there run no lake outflows. Philipson (1954) has shown that *H. instabilis* requires a certain minimum current before it will spin its net; and it is certainly true that this species occurs in the River Endrick only where the current is strong.

Plectrocnemia conspersa (Curtis) has a very limited distribution in the main river and is found only in the upper reaches. King (1901) recorded it from Ballagan Burn. It is most common among moss, and is especially abundant in this habitat at station 12 (Source). Both Mackereth (1960) and Hynes (1961) also found that this species was most common in the upper parts of the streams which they studied.

Polycentropus flavomaculatus (Pictet) occurs in all parts of the river except the extreme lower reaches. It is a very common species, especially in the middle reaches, where it is abundant under stones both in riffle where the current is strong and in pools where it is weaker. In the upper reaches this species tends to be replaced by *Plectrocnemia conspersa*. Adults are common among vegetation at the edge of the river during summer.

Polycentropus multiguttatus (Curtis) is a very rare species in the River Endrick, a single larva having been collected among stones in shallow water at station 5 (Drumtian) in the middle reaches.

Cyrnus trimaculatus (Curtis). The larvae of this species have been found only in the middle reaches of the river, where they are common but never abundant among the silt layer on stones near the edges of pools, where the current is slow. Adults were collected occasionally among vegetation at the edge of the river near station 5 (Drumtian).

Tinodes waeneri (L.). Larvae of *Tinodes* occur only in the middle reaches of the river, where they are found frequently among stones in pools where the current is slow. Adults of *T. waeneri* are common among vegetation at the edge of the river here, and King (1901) has recorded this species from the Ballagan Burn—a tributary of the Blane Water.

Lype phaeopa (Stephens). A single adult of this species was collected among vegetation at the edge of the river near station 5 (Drumtian) in the middle reaches.

Psychomyia pusilla (Fabricius) is found in all parts of the river except the extreme upper and the extreme lower reaches. Larvae are common among stones in pools where the current is slow, whilst adults have been taken among marginal vegetation in the middle reaches during summer.

Philopotamus montanus (Donovan). A single larva of this species was collected among stones in riffle at station 10 (Cringate) in the upper reaches. It has, however, been found to be abundant in a similar habitat in Gonachan Burn, the first tributary of importance to enter the river on its left bank (Fig. 2). King (1901) records this species from Ballagan Burn.

Rhyacophila dorsalis (Curtis) occurs in all parts of the river except the extreme lower and the extreme upper reaches, being most common among stones in riffle in the middle reaches. Adults are common among vegetation at the edge of the river during summer.

Rhyacophila septentrionis (McLachlan) is a rare species in the River Endrick, and only two specimens have been collected so far: both were taken as larvae among stones in riffle in the middle reaches of the river.

Rhyacophila munda (McLachlan) is restricted to the upper reaches of the river, but unlike *R. dorsalis* it is not found among stones in riffle here, occurring instead mainly among moss—a habitat also inhabited by *R. dorsalis*.

Glossosoma boltoni (Curtis) occurs only in the middle reaches of the river, where it is found attached to stones in pools. It has also been collected from a similar habitat in the Blane Water, but is never an abundant species.

Agapetus fuscipes (Curtis) is common only in the middle reaches of the river, where it is mostly found attached to stones in pools, and in places may be extremely abundant. Often the surfaces of such stones are completely covered by the cases of this species, which is also common in many of the tributary streams entering the River Endrick. King (1901) has recorded it from Ballagan Burn.

Agapetus delicatulus (McLachlan), adults of which were collected among vegetation at the edge of the river near station 5 (Drumtian) in the middle reaches, has not been found as a larva so far.

Agraylea multipunctata (Curtis) occurs only in the lower reaches of the river, where the larvae are common, but never abundant, among weed growing in silt in shallow water.

Hydroptila occulta (Eaton). Larvae of *Hydroptila* are found in all parts of the river except the extreme upper and lower reaches. They occur in a variety of habitats, but are most common among stones in riffle and among moss in the middle reaches, where large aggregations of larvae can often be found attached to a single stone or piece of moss. Adults of *H. occulta* have been collected among vegetation at the edge of the middle reaches of the river, but never appear to be common.

Hydroptila forcipata (Eaton). Adults of this species were collected among vegetation at the edge of the river in the middle reaches near station 5 (Drumtian), whilst larvae found among small stones in riffle in the Altquhur Burn and reared in the laboratory also proved to be this species.

Lepidoptera

Only one species of this group is known to occur in the river.

Nymphula nymphaeata (L.) occurs only in the extreme lower reaches of the river, where the larvae are common during summer on the undersurface of the leaves of *Nuphar lutea*—on which they feed. The silken shelter which each builds is protected above by the leaf itself, and below by an oval piece of that leaf which the larva has bitten out. By means of the characteristic holes which are left in the leaves it is usually possible to determine the number of *N. nymphaeata* larvae present in any given group of *Nuphar*.

Diptera

This group is undoubtedly one of the most important in the River Endrick, its members forming a large part of the fauna in all habitats. Unfortunately, it is impossible at present to identify the great majority of the larvae to species—apart from Simuliidae and a few small families (Fig. 41). As with Trichoptera, this difficulty has been partly overcome in the present study by rearing larvae in the laboratory and collecting adults beside the river. It is certain, however, that

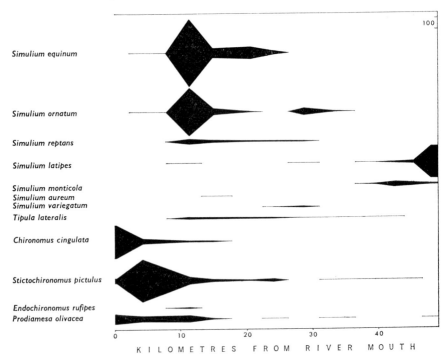

Fig. 41.—The distribution of common Diptera in the River Endrick

there are many more species yet to be determined, and the list of forty-eight discussed below is in no sense a complete one. The following genera, for example, have all been found in the river as larvae, but none has yet been identified to species: *Dicranota, Limnophora, Hemerodromia, Pericoma, Ephydra, Pedicia, Atherix, Chrysops, Dixa, Bezzia, Culicoides, Macropelopia, Trichocladius,* and *Cardiocladius.*

Simulium equinum (L.) occurs only in the lower half of the river, though it is not found downstream as far as the mouth. It is common where the current is fast, usually among weed or stones, and in places may be very abundant.

Simulium ornatum (Meigen). The distribution and occurrence of this species are very similar to those of *S. equinum*, and in places it is equally abundant.

Simulium reptans (L.) also has a distribution and occurrence similar to those of *S. equinum*, though it is always less common than that species. The variety *galeratum* Edwards is found in places, and may form up to 50 per cent of the *S. reptans* population. Smart (1944) notes that this variety has been previously recorded in Britain only from the River Ox.

Simulium latipes (Meigen) is common only in the upper reaches of the river, being particularly abundant at station 12 (Source). Here, it occurs among moss and also among gravel and peat in riffle.

Simulium monticola (Friederichs) too occurs only in the upper reaches of the river, where it is common but never abundant among moss and stones in riffle.

Simulium aureum (Fries). In the main river this species has been found only at station 5 (Drumtian) in the middle reaches, where two pupae were collected from stones in riffle. It is common, however, in the Catter and Altquhur Burns, also among stones in riffle.

Simulium variegatum (Meigen) occurs only in the middle reaches of the river, where it is found attached to large stones in places where the current is strong. It is never a common species, however.

Tipula lateralis (Meigen) is common only in the lower reaches of the river, though it does not occur as far downstream as the mouth. It is found mostly among coarse gravel, both in riffle and at the edge where it is more silted.

Culex pipiens (L.). A single larva of this species was collected in the lower reaches of the river at station 2 (Woodend) among weed growing in silt in shallow water.

Pentaneura carnea (Fabricius). Larvae of *Pentaneura* are common in all parts of the river. In the lower reaches at station 2 (Woodend) they occur among sand and silt in deep water, and adults reared from larvae collected here proved to be *P. carnea*.

Procladius choreus (Meigen) adults were reared from larvae also collected at station 2 (Woodend) from among sand and silt. Larvae of *Procladius* are common only in the lower reaches of the river, though they do occur occasionally further upstream.

Stictochironomus pictulus (Meigen). Larvae of *Stictochironomus* are common in the lower reaches of the river among silt, and also in similar conditions further upstream, although this habitat is much rarer there. Numerous adults, all identified as *S. pictulus*, were reared from larvae collected in the lower reaches at station 2 (Woodend).

Chironomus cingulatus (Meigen) adults were also reared from larvae collected at station 2. Larvae of *Chironomus* are common only in the lower reaches of the river, especially in the fine silt which is abundant just above the mouth.

Chironomus anthracinus (Zetterstedt). A single adult of this species was collected beside Finnich Burn (Fig. 2) among overhanging vegetation.

Cryptochironomus digitalis (Edwards). Larvae of *Cryptochironomus* were collected on various occasions in the lower reaches of the river mostly among weed. Adults of *C. digitalis* were collected among emergent vegetation during the summer months near station 2 (Woodend).

Cryptochironomus cinctellus (Goetghebuer) adults were also collected among vegetation near station 2 (Woodend) in the lower reaches of the river.

Endochironomus rufipes (L.). Larvae of *Endochironomus* are found in the middle and lower reaches of the river, where they occur mostly among weed but never appear to be common. A single male of *E. rufipes*, a large and characteristic species, was collected among bushes at the edge of the river near station 3 (Drymen). Large red larvae collected among *Ephydatia* at this station were reared and found to be this species.

Microtendipes fuscus (Meigen). Larvae of *Microtendipes* are common in the lower reaches of the river among weed growing in silt. Adults of *M. fuscus* were collected early in 1962 among dead vegetation at the edge of the river in the lower reaches.

Polypedilum scalaenus (Schrank). Larvae of *Polypedilum* were collected occasionally among stones in riffle at station 5 (Drumtian) in the middle reaches of the river; adults of *P. scalaenus* var. *quadriguttatus* Kieffer were taken at this same station among vegetation growing on the river bank.

Polypedilum albicornis (Meigen.) Adults of this species were collected occasionally at the edge of the river in the lower reaches.

Tanytarsus curticornis (Kieffer). Larvae of *Tanytarsus* are very common in all parts of the river, especially the lower reaches. Adults reared in the laboratory from larvae collected among quantitative samples of sand and silt (see Maitland, 1964a) from station 2 (Woodend) proved to be *T. curticornis*.

Tanytarsus mancus (Walker). Adults of this species are very common among emergent vegetation in the lower reaches of the river during summer.

Tanytarsus inopertus (Walker) adults were collected occasionally among vegetation beside the lower reaches of the river and also beside some of the tributaries.

Tanytarsus holochlorus (Edwards.) A single adult male, identified as this species, was found among emergent vegetation in the Blane Water (Fig. 2).

Micropsectra atrofasciatus (Kieffer) adults are common at the edge of the river in the lower reaches during summer.

Prodiamesa olivacea (Meigen) is common only in the lower reaches of the river, though it may also occur upstream in the vicinity of sewage effluents (Maitland, 1962b). The larvae are most common among fine silt in shallow water, whilst adults are common along the edge of the river in the lower reaches. Adults were also reared from larvae collected among sand and silt at station 2 (Woodend).

Diamesa culicoides (Hegeer). Larvae of *Diamesa* are common in the lower reaches of the river among algae growing on stones where the current is slow. Adults identified as *D. culicoides* were collected in some numbers among vegetation at the edge of the Finnich Burn— in which *Diamesa* larvae are also known to occur.

Diamesa permacer (Walker). A single adult male of this species was collected from a swarm at the edge of the river in the upper reaches near station 11 (Burnfoot).

Potthastia longimanus (Kieffer) is also recorded only from a single male specimen, which was collected among emergent vegetation in the lower reaches of the river near station 2 (Woodend).

Brillia modesta (Meigen) has been recorded only from the middle reaches of the river, where a single adult male was taken near the edge at station 5 (Drumtian).

Brillia longifurca (Kieffer). Several adults of this species were collected among vegetation at the edge of the Blane Water (Fig. 2), near its junction with the main river, during the summer months.

Orthocladius oblidens (Walker). Larvae of *Orthocladius* are common in all parts of the river, especially where plant growths occur, and several distinct types have been recognized, but not yet related to adult species. Adults of *O. oblidens* were collected in some numbers among emergent vegetation in the lower reaches of the river during winter, near station 1 (Mouth).

Orthocladius rubicundus (Meigen) adults are common during summer among vegetation at the edge of the river near station 5 (Drumtian) in the middle reaches.

Chaetocladius piger (Goetghebuer). Adults of this species were collected among vegetation at the edge of the river near several stations in the middle reaches.

Paralimnophyes hydrophilus (Goetghebuer) adults have been collected among emergent vegetation near station 2 (Woodend) in the lower reaches of the river, and near station 5 (Drumtian) in the middle reaches.

Limnophyes pusillus (Eaton). Several adult specimens of this species were collected among vegetation beside the Altquhur Burn (Fig. 2).

Smittia nudipennis (Goetghebuer). A single adult male of this species was collected among vegetation at the edge of the river near station 5 (Drumtian) in the middle reaches.

Heterotrissocladius marcidus (Walker) is also recorded from a single adult male, which was taken at the edge of the river near station 2 (Woodend) in the lower reaches.

Cricotopus trifasciatus (Panzer). Larvae of *Cricotopus* are known to occur in the middle reaches of the river among stones in riffle. They are uncommon, however, whilst the adults of this genus are very common during summer in all parts of the river valley. It would appear, therefore, that the optimum habitat of the larvae has not yet been discovered, or more probably that the larvae have been mis-identified as another genus—possibly one of the types of *Orthocladius* mentioned above. Adults of *C. trifasciatus* are common among vegetation at the edges of the lower reaches of the river.

Cricotopus tremulus (L.) is the most common member of the genus, and adults are common in spring and summer along the banks of the river both in the lower and the middle reaches.

Rheocricotopus dispar (Goetghebuer) adults were collected among emergent vegetation in the lower reaches of the river, near station 1 (Mouth) during the early spring.

Syncricotopus rufiventris (Meigen). Adults of this species were taken occasionally during summer among vegetation at the edge of the river in the middle reaches near station 5 (Drumtian).

Corynoneura scutellata (Winnertz). The minute larvae of *Corynoneura* are common among weed in the lower and middle reaches of the River Endrick. Several adult specimens of *C. scutellata* were collected among emergent vegetation in the lower reaches near station 2 (Woodend).

Metriocnemus fuscipes (Meigen). Larvae of *Metriocnemus* occur in the lower and middle reaches of the river among weed, but never appear to be common. In the lower reaches during summer adults of *M. fuscipes* were collected among emergent vegetation.

Metriocnemus ursinus (Holmgren). A single adult male of this species was collected at the edge of the river near station 5 (Drumtian) in the middle reaches.

Metriocnemus martinii (Thum) too is recorded from a single male collected among vegetation in the middle reaches of the river near station 5 (Drumtian).

Metriocnemus atratulus (Zetterstedt) is also recorded from a single specimen, this time a female, which was collected among emergent vegetation in the lower reaches of the river, near station 2 (Woodend).

Eukiefferiella ilkleyensis (Edwards). The larvae of *Eukiefferiella* are common in all parts of the river, especially the middle reaches, where they are abundant among stones in riffle and among weed. Though only one species has been found in the adult stage there are several distinct types of larvae. Adults identified as *E. ilkleyensis* were collected during the summer months at the edge of the river in the middle reaches, near station 5 (Drumtian).

Coleoptera

This group is found in all parts of the river. It is least important in the lower reaches, but in the middle and upper reaches forms an important part of the invertebrate fauna in most habitats (Fig. 4J).

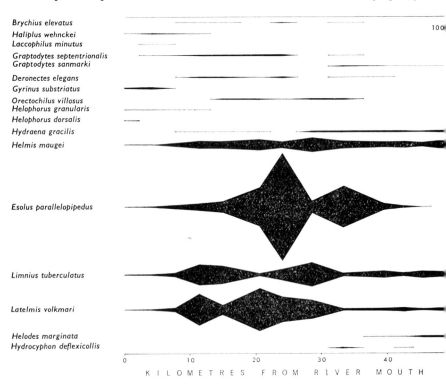

Fig. 4J.—The distribution of common Coleoptera in the River Endrick

A wide variety of type occurs and altogether some forty species have been recorded, though many of them on only one or two occasions.

Brychius elevatus (Panzer) occurs in the lower and middle reaches, though it does not extend downstream as far as the mouth. It is never an abundant species, and unlike the two species of *Haliplus* below seems to be able to withstand a strong current—being most common among stones in riffle.

Haliplus lineatocollis (Marsham). Two specimens of this species were collected in the lower reaches of the river at station 3 (Drymen) among *Elodea canadensis* growing in silt.

Haliplus wehnckei (Gerhardt) occurs only in the lower reaches of the river, where during summer it is common among weed growing in silt.

Hygrotus inaequalis (Fabricius). A single specimen of this species was collected in the lower reaches of the river at station 1 (Mouth) among weed growing in silt.

Laccophilus minutus (L.) is restricted to the lower reaches of the river, where several specimens have been taken among weed growing in silt. It is not a common species, however.

Graptodytes septentrionalis (Gyllenhal) occurs in both the lower and the middle reaches of the river. It is common among gravel and small stones in shallow water at the edges of pools, where the current is slow.

Graptodytes sanmarki (Sahlberg) is found only in the middle and upper reaches of the river, where it occurs in small numbers in a habitat similar to that occupied by the previous species further downstream.

Deronectes elegans (Panzer) occurs only in the lower and middle reaches of the river, where it is common among weed growing in silt and also among silted gravel and stones in pools.

Hydroporus palustris (L.) has been found only in the lower reaches of the river, where it is common among floating logs and other debris near the edge.

Hydroporus rufifrons (Müller). Three specimens of this species were collected in the lower reaches of the river at station 2 (Woodend), from the undersurface of a floating log. A single specimen was found also at the edge of the Maucher Burn underneath a stone in shallow water.

Hydroporus melanarius (Sturm). A single specimen of this species was collected in the upper reaches of the river at station 11 (Burnfoot) among stones in shallow water.

Hydroporus ferrugineus (Stephens) is also very uncommon, a single specimen having been collected in the lower reaches of the river at station 4 (Dalnair), underneath a stone in shallow slow-flowing water.

Agabus guttatus (Paykull) has been found in several places in the middle and upper reaches of the river. All were collected as single specimens among stones and gravel in shallow water.

Agabus bipustulatus (L.) has been recorded only once in the River Endrick, when a single specimen was collected in the lower reaches at station 1 (Mouth), among weed growing in silt.

Platambus maculatus (L.) occurs in all parts of the river except the extreme lower reaches. It is most common among gravel and stones in shallow, fast-flowing water in the middle reaches.

Ilybius ater (Degeer) has never been recorded from the main river, though a single specimen was found in shallow water at the edge of the Burn of Mar.

Gyrinus substriatus (Stephens) occurs only in the lower reaches of the river where adults are common during summer, often congregating in large numbers at the surface of the water, particularly under over-hanging trees. *Gyrinus* larvae occur among weed growing in silt in this part of the river, but they are never common.

Orectochilus villosus (Müller) is found only in the middle reaches of the river. The adults are nocturnal, and during the day occur in small numbers under stones at the edge of the river, just above the water level; the larvae occur among stones in riffle but are never abundant, whilst the eggs have been found on only one occasion— attached to the undersurface of a stone in shallow water at station 7 (Dalfoil).

Anacaena limbata (Fabricius) occurs in the lower and middle reaches of the river, where it is common, but never abundant, among stones in silt at the edges of pools.

Laccobius biguttatus (Gerhardt). A single specimen of this species was found in the lower reaches of the river at station 4 (Dalnair) among silted gravel in shallow water.

Laccobius minutus (L.) is found only in the lower reaches, where it occurs regularly but never abundantly in shallow water among silted gravel at the edge of the river.

Laccobius ytenensis (Sharp). A single specimen of this species was collected in the lower reaches of the river at station 3 (Drymen) among silted boulders in slow-flowing water.

Limnebius truncatellus (Thunberg) occurs occasionally in the middle and upper reaches of the river. Specimens have been taken among stones in riffle and among moss in shallow water here, and on one occasion a single adult was collected among flood-drift at station 2 (Woodend) in the lower reaches.

Limnebius papposus (Mulsant) is a very uncommon species in the River Endrick, single specimens having been collected only in the upper reaches at station 11 (Burnfoot), and in the Maucher Burn under stones in shallow water.

Helophorus aquaticus (L.). Two specimens of this species were collected in the middle reaches of the river at station 5 (Drumtian) underneath stones in shallow water.

Helophorus affinis (Marsham) is uncommon in the River Endrick and has never been recorded from the main river. A single specimen was collected, however, under a stone in shallow water at the edge of Balglass Burn.

Helophorus granularis (L.) is common only in the lower reaches of the river, where it occurs among weed growing in silt in shallow water. Occasional specimens have been recorded under stones in shallow water further upstream.

Helophorus dorsalis (Marsham) is uncommon and has been found only in the lower reaches at station 1 (Mouth), where several specimens were collected among weed growing in silt at the edge of the river.

Hydraena nigrita (Germar). A single specimen of this species was collected in the lower reaches of the river at station 3 (Drymen) among *Myriophyllum* growing in gravel.

Hydraena gracilis (Germar) occurs in the middle and upper reaches of the river, being most common among stones in riffle in the upper reaches.

Helmis maugei (Bedel) is found in all parts of the river, though it is least common in the lower reaches. It occurs in a variety of habitats

—notably stones in riffle and moss, where both larvae and adults occur in large numbers.

Esolus parallelopipedus (Müller) occurs in all parts of the river except the extreme upper reaches, where it is found in several habitats, particularly algae growing on stones where the current is fast enough to prevent the deposition of silt. Under such conditions both larvae and adults may be abundant.

Limnius tuberculatus (Müller) is one of the most widespread invertebrate species in the River Endrick and occurs in a variety of habitats in all reaches. It appears to be more tolerant of silted conditions than *E. parallelopipedus*, occurring among weed growing in silt and silted gravel in the lower reaches, as well as among moss and stones in other parts of the river.

Riolus cupreus (Müller). A single larva of this species was collected in the lower reaches of the river at station 3 (Drymen) among stones in riffle. Weerekoon (1956) has recorded it also from Loch Lomond.

Latelmis volkmari (Panzer) occurs in all parts of the river, but is not common in the lower reaches. In other parts of the river both larvae and adults may be abundant among stones in riffle and among moss.

Dryops ernesti (Des Gozis) has never been found in the main river; two specimens, however, were found under stones in shallow water at the edge of Balglass Burn.

Helodes marginata (Fabricius) is found only in the upper reaches of the river, where it is common, but never abundant, among stones in riffle and among moss.

Hydrocyphon deflexicollis (Müller) occurs in a restricted stretch of the river in the upper reaches. It never extends upstream as far as the source and occurs mostly under stones in riffle.

Donacia versicolorea (Brahm). A single specimen of this species was collected from the floating leaves of *Potamogeton natans* in the lower reaches of the river near station 1 (Mouth). It has also been observed on *P. natans* in small pools in the Strathblane area of the Endrick valley.

Donacia simplex (Fabricius) occurs only in the lower reaches of the river, where the adults are common during summer on the leaves of *Sparganium ramosum*, which grows in silt here at the river's edge.

Arthropoda—Arachnida

Hydracarina

This group occurs in most parts of the river, but its members rarely form a large part of the invertebrate population (Fig. 4к). Fourteen species have so far been recorded.

Sperchon glandulosus (Koenike) is found among weed growing over silt in the lower reaches of the river, but is never a very common species.

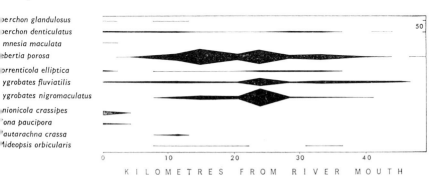

Fig. 4к.—The distribution of common Hydracarina in the River Endrick

Sperchon denticulatus (Koenike) occurs in all parts of the river except the extreme upper reaches. It is most common among moss and algae growing on stones but is never abundant.

Limnesia maculata (Müller) has been found only in the lower reaches of the river at station 1 (Mouth), where several specimens were collected among weed growing in silt.

Lebertia porosa (Thor) occurs in all parts of the river, and in some places may be abundant. Its optimum habitat appears to be among algae and silt on stones and gravel in the lower reaches of the river.

Torrenticola elliptica (Maglio) is common among stones and gravel in the middle and lower reaches of the river, even where the current is strong. It is never abundant, however.

Torrenticola amplexa (Koenike) occurs only in the lower reaches of the river and even here is uncommon. Several specimens were collected among *Myriophyllum* growing in gravel at station 3 (Drymen).

Atractides tener (Maglio) has been found only in the upper reaches of the river, where several specimens were collected among stones in riffle at station 11 (Burnfoot).

Hygrobates fluviatilis (Ström) occurs in all parts of the river, but is most abundant in the middle and lower reaches among weed and stones in silted areas.

Hygrobates nigromaculatus (Lebert) also occurs in most parts of the river, though it is absent from the extreme upper and lower reaches. Occurring most commonly among stones and gravel in riffle, it is never an abundant species.

Unionicola crassipes (Müller) occurs only in the lower reaches of the river, where it is common among weed growing in silt. This distribution agrees with the fact that the larvae of this species are parasitic on *Ephydatia fluviatilis* (Hopkins, 1962), for it is only here that the latter species is common.

Piona paucipora (Thor) is found only in the lower reaches of the river, being common among weed in silt at station 1 (Mouth).

Nautarachna crassa (Koenike). Several specimens of this species, which is uncommon in the river, were collected from among *Elodea* growing in silt at station 3 (Drymen) in the lower reaches. This is the only station at which the species has been found.

Mideopsis orbicularis (Müller) occurs in both the middle and the lower reaches of the river, having been found there in a number of habitats. This species appears to be most common among stones and gravel in riffle, but is never abundant.

Notaspis lacustris (Michael). The few specimens of this species which have been taken so far occurred singly, among stones in riffle in the middle and lower reaches of the river.

Mollusca

Members of this group occur in most parts of the river and in some habitats they form an important part of the invertebrate fauna. Only a few species are widespread, however, the great majority being confined to the lower reaches (Fig. 4L). This is presumably related to the fact that most freshwater Mollusca require a certain amount of calcium in the water (Boycott, 1936), and only three species have been found where the calcium content of the water is less than

10 mg./l. (i.e. above the lower reaches of the river)—*A. fluviatilis,*
L. pereger, and *P. casertanum.* Altogether, seventeen species have
been recorded from the River Endrick during the present survey.
Hunter (1958) recorded a single shell of *Margaritifera margaritifera*
(L.) from the Stirlingshire bank of the Endrick mouth, but in spite
of careful search this species has never been found in the river by the
author.

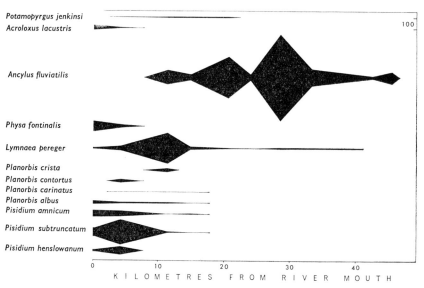

Fig. 4L.—The distribution of common Mollusca in the River Endrick

Valvata piscinalis (Müller). A single specimen of this species was
collected in the lower reaches of the river at station 1 (Mouth) among
weed growing in silt. Weerekoon (1956) records it as being common
in Loch Lomond.

Potamopyrgus jenkinsi (Smith) is common only in the lower reaches
of the river, though occasional specimens have been taken at station 5
(Drumtian) in the middle reaches. It has not previously been recorded from this watershed, and its occurrence is reported in
full elsewhere (Hunter, Maitland and Yeoh, 1963). *P. jenkinsi* is most
abundant among stable boulders in slightly silted conditions, being
one of several species (discussed below) which are common in the

main river below its junction with the Blane Water, but very un-common above this point.

Acroloxus lacustris (L.) occurs only in the extreme lower reaches of the river, where it is found among weed growing in silt, being particularly common attached to the stems and leaves of *Nuphar* and *Polygonum*. Hunter (1954) has recorded this species from only one place in Loch Lomond—some 400 metres north of the mouth of the River Endrick; it appears to be absent elsewhere in the loch, and it seems highly probable that this population is in fact derived from that in the River Endrick.

Ancylus fluviatilis (Müller) is undoubtedly the most abundant species of mollusc in the River Endrick, being found in all parts except the extreme upper and the extreme lower reaches. It is the only mollusc which is common in the middle and upper reaches of the river, occurring even where the calcium content of the water is con-siderably less than 5 mg./l. Stable stones in current, where there is little deposition of silt, seem to offer it an optimum habitat.

Though closely related, *Acroloxus lacustris* and *Ancylus fluviatilis* show a distinct contrast in habitat. Contrary, perhaps, to what might be expected, Berg (1952) has shown that the oxygen requirements of the two species are almost identical. He has, however, pointed out a distinct difference in the behaviour of the two species under conditions of low oxygen tension—*A. lacustris* showing a much greater capacity to climb upwards than *A. fluviatilis*. This observation accounts in part for the differences of habitat between the two species—the ability to climb upwards out of anaerobic muds being an obvious advantage to *A. lacustris* for life in the silted lower reaches of the river.

Physa fontinalis (L.) occurs only in the extreme lower reaches of the river, where it is very common among weed growing in silt. During summer its egg masses are abundant on the undersurface of the leaves of *Nuphar lutea*.

Lymnaea truncatula (Müller). Only two specimens of this species have been found in the River Endrick: both were collected in the lower reaches of the river at station 2 (Woodend) among weed growing in silt in shallow water.

Lymnaea pereger (Müller) occurs in the middle and lower reaches of the river. It is most common in the lower reaches, among weed and stones in silt; in the middle reaches only occasional specimens occur among stones in shallow water.

Planorbis crista (L.) is found only in the lower reaches of the river, where it is common among weed growing in silt.

Planorbis contortus (L.) is also restricted to the lower reaches of the river, where it too is common among weed growing in silt.

Planorbis carinatus (Müller) occurs uncommonly in the lower reaches of the river, where specimens have been collected among weed growing in silt and also from stones in silted conditions at the edge.

Planorbis albus (Müller) is also found only in the lower reaches of the river, among weed growing in silt. It is especially abundant in this habitat at station 1 (Mouth).

Anodonta anatina (L.). This large bivalve occurs only in the lower reaches of the river, where specimens have been collected at many places. It never appears to be abundant, however, and, whilst all the specimens taken so far were found among silt at the edge of the river, it appears probable that the bulk of the population lives in deeper water. Hunter (1954) records this species from the River Endrick on the basis of a single specimen found by Dr. H. D. Slack in the lower reaches, near station 3 (Drymen); in a later publication (1958) the same author records the occurrence of many specimens near the mouth of the river during conditions of extreme low water.

Pisidium amnicum (Müller) is found only in the lower reaches of the river, where it is common among weed growing in silt near the edge, and also among bare silt, both at the edge of the river and in midstream. Hunter (1958) has also recorded this species from the lower Endrick.

Pisidium subtruncatum (Malm) is also found only in the lower reaches of the river, occurring here among sand and silt in all parts of the river bed.

Pisidium henslowanum (Sheppard) occurs only in the extreme lower reaches of the river, where it is found in the same type of substrate as the two previous species. Hunter (1958) also records it from the lower Endrick.

It is of some interest to note that Boycott (1936) has pointed out that the above three species of *Pisidium* often occur in association with each other, mostly in running water; the present records are in agreement with this observation.

Pisidium casertanum (Poli) has been found in most parts of the middle and upper reaches of the River Endrick, but never in great numbers. Hunter and Hamilton (1958) note that *P. casertanum* is ubiquitous throughout Great Britain, and Hunter (1958) records it as being very common in Loch Lomond and western Scotland.

Sphaerium corneum (L.). A few specimens only of this species have been found in the lower reaches of the river, where they were collected among weed growing in silt.

Ectoprocta—Phylactolaemata

These form a very insignificant part of the fauna and rarely occurred in collections taken by normal methods. Only three species are known to occur, these being found in the lower and middle reaches of the river.

Plumatella repens (L.) occurs only in the lower reaches of the river, where it is common in certain habitats—notably the undersurfaces of stones and the leaves of *Nuphar lutea*.

Cristatella mucedo (Cuvier) has never been found in the main river. Statoblasts of this species, however, were taken from the stomach of a Minnow caught in Loch Walton, the outflow from which enters the middle reaches of the River Endrick. Weerekoon (1956) has also recorded statoblasts of *C. mucedo* in Loch Lomond but has never found the adult colonies there.

Fredericella sultana (Blumenbach) has been found only in the middle reaches of the river, where at station 8 (Culcreuch) colonies were abundant among *Fontinalis* in slowly-flowing water.

Plate IIIA.—The upper reaches of the River Endrick at station 11 (Burnfoot) looking upstream in summer. The current in most places here is fast and the substrate consists mainly of bare rock and large moss-covered boulders. Small waterfalls with pools below them, as seen in the background here, are common in this part of the river. Brown Trout are the only fish found in this stretch

Plate IIIB.—The extreme upper reaches of the River Endrick at station 12 (Source) looking upstream in winter; near here the river rises in the Gargunnock Hills. The water is shallow in this stretch; the bottom consists for the most part of peat with some small stones. The only fish occurring here are Brown Trout, and even these are uncommon

Plate IVA.—*Arcteonais lomondi*. This species was first described from Loch Lomond by Martin (1907), who named it accordingly; in Great Britain it is still known only from parts of Loch Lomond and the extreme lower reaches of the River Endrick. It occurs most commonly among fine organic silts. The short proboscis and the paired clumps of fine setae shown here are characteristic of this species of Oligochaeta, (× 100)

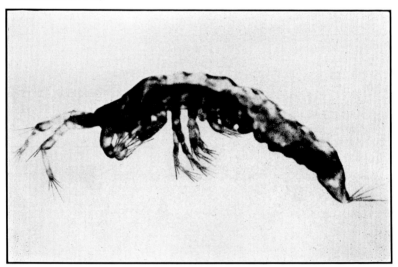

Plate IVB.—*Bathynella natans*. This small blind member of the Crustacea has been found in Scotland only in the Altquhur Burn, one of the main tributaries of the Endrick system (Maitland, 1962a). This species is a rather primitive form which normally lives underground in the interstitial water occurring among large deposits of coarse sand and gravel (Plate VIA). The specimen shown here is a late larval stage, (× 100)

III. INVERTEBRATE BIOTOPES

In any critical evaluation of the fauna of a river it is necessary to determine the importance of each group of animals to the various communities present. The distribution and abundance of each invertebrate species known to occur in the River Endrick are discussed above, the present section dealing merely with the general composition of the fauna found in the main habitats in the river. In particular, the relationships of such habitats to the general features of invertebrate distribution within the river system are examined.

The collecting methods and material relating to this account have been described above; only collections from habitats in the main river are included, these being compared and discussed on a percentage composition basis. The percentage composition of the fauna in any given habitat has been assessed in an arbitrary manner by averaging the percentage compositions of the total invertebrate fauna found there in February, June and October.

Main Biotopes

Only the more important biotopes occurring in the River Endrick are discussed here; these are classified into rather general types, there being no attempt to subdivide them on a microhabitat basis. Thus collections from any type of aquatic vegetation (referred to generally as "weed") includes animals which live among weed, attached to weed and even within weed, all being classified as living in a weed biotope. The habitats examined vary from those which possess few niches (microhabitats), e.g. bare silt, to those which possess many, e.g. riffle. Differences between such habitats are discussed elsewhere (Maitland, 1964a) in connection with quantitative studies, where it is shown that substrates which offer a large number of ecological niches possess more species and are more productive than those with fewer niches. Even with biotopes which are of a general nature, it is

67

of prime importance to consider the factors which influence their formation and existence. Each biotope possesses its own primary physical and chemical characteristics—current, depth, temperature, oxygen, calcium, etc.—which may vary in importance to each member of its community.

Almost all workers on the biology of rivers have noted that the influence of the current is one of the most important factors in any habitat; on it depends whether a substrate will be stable or unstable, silted or unsilted, and whether weed (and what species of weed) can grow or not, etc. (Butcher, 1933). The results from the quantitative studies described below also emphasize the importance of current speed—particularly in connection with turbulence and the stability of the substrate. Percival and Whitehead (1929) noted that current was probably the most important factor in determining the nature of the substrate at any one point. In view of the difficulty, however, of estimating the current speed at any one place, and its rapid variation, even in a short space of time, they rejected current measurement in favour of a direct description of the substrate when defining habitat types in a river. This method of evaluation has also been adopted in the present study, owing to the variation in current speed recorded during the quantitative studies described below.

The substrates found in the River Endrick vary from fine silt to large boulders with all gradations between these types. In some places weeds establish themselves and may alter the original substrate considerably, as well as providing additional food and cover for many invertebrate species. The habitat referred to here as riffle is a rather complex one, consisting mostly of coarse gravel and stones in places where the current is swift enough for the water surface to be turbulent and broken. Though little silting occurs here there is often a tendency for drift material (dead leaves etc.) to collect between the stones, and this may form a valuable source of food for some groups—e.g. many species of Plecoptera are known to occur in large numbers among such leaf packets (Hynes, 1941).

The eight biotopes included in Table 2 are the commonest and most important in the River Endrick, and it is only in the lower reaches that all eight occur in reasonable proximity to one another. Riffle is probably the most important type, occupying large areas of the river bed above the extreme lower reaches. Silt, on the other hand, occurs commonly only in the extreme lower reaches, though small areas of it are occasionally found further upstream, notably at the edges of pools. (The effect of these small areas may, however, be important locally—as was established during the study of certain fish feeding relationships (Maitland, 1965)). Weed grows both where the current is fast and where it is slow or absent, though the species of plant vary accordingly. The distinction of habitat made here is essentially between weed which grows in current and weed which grows where there is none. Emergent and floating-leaved forms are characteristic of the latter type of habitat. Gravel occurs particularly in the lower reaches of the river above Drymen, and in some stretches here may cover the whole of the stream bed; that at the edges of pools tends to silt rapidly during the summer and is also affected greatly by fluctuations in the water level. This type of substrate appears to be very unstable, for large areas of gravel are often moved during spates. Larger stones occur both in very fast current and in stretches where the current is slow. Those in the former are nearly always clean and smooth (except where moss cover is present), whilst on those where the current is slow a thick coating of silt is usually present—especially during summer.

Characteristic Fauna

Though most of the important groups of freshwater invertebrates occur in the lower reaches of the River Endrick, several of them are uncommon and make up only a small percentage of the fauna as a whole. These include Coelenterata, Platyhelminthes, Plecoptera, Odonata, Neuroptera, Trichoptera, Lepidoptera and Hydracarina. Many of the members of these groups occur only sporadically, whilst others, though never becoming abundant, do occur regularly and may be characteristic of a particular habitat. This is true of Lepidoptera and Odonata which are found only among weed growing in silt in the lower reaches.

Table 2 shows the distribution of different invertebrate groups in the main habitats of the lower reaches of the river. Oligochaeta are common in all biotopes, especially in those which tend to be silted,

Table 2.—Percentage composition of the invertebrate fauna of the main biotopes in the lower reaches of the River Endrick

Invertebrate Fauna	Riffle Current	Silt Pool	Weed Current	Weed Pool	Gravel Current	Gravel Pool	Stones Current	Stones Pool
Coelenterata	0·1	0·1	0·1	0·1	0·2	—	—	0·5
Platyhelminthes	0·1	—	0·1	1·1	0·1	0·1	0·1	0·5
Oligochaeta	16·2	30·5	10·0	15·3	3·4	35·9	5·6	2·9
Hirudinea	5·6	0·4	0·7	0·3	—	2·6	0·1	3·8
Crustacea	3·8	2·3	6·0	17·4	5·3	4·4	7·6	6·2
Ephemeroptera	12·4	2·8	7·4	9·9	16·7	3·9	12·1	3·4
Plecoptera	1·9	0·1	0·4	0·2	5·1	0·3	1·2	0·1
Odonata	—	—	—	0·9	—	—	—	—
Hemiptera	—	14·1	—	14·4	—	0·1	—	0·1
Neuroptera	—	—	—	—	—	—	—	0·1
Trichoptera	0·4	1·7	0·4	2·0	0·1	0·1	0·6	5·1
Lepidoptera	—	—	—	0·1	—	—	—	—
Diptera	39·2	38·1	59·8	26·1	48·0	49·7	58·2	41·3
Coleoptera	11·4	0·7	3·6	1·4	14·2	2·1	7·5	18·1
Hydracarina	0·3	0·5	2·2	0·8	0·2	0·5	0·9	8·6
Mollusca	8·6	8·7	9·3	10·0	6·7	0·3	6·1	9·3
No. Samples	9	6	6	9	3	6	3	6
Ave. No. Sample	1312	735	1888	1386	2060	1575	1266	1068

whilst Hirudinea are found only on the more stable substrates and are rarely numerous. In most habitats, Crustacea are common, being especially abundant among weed in still water where various Entomostraca are numerous during the summer. Large numbers of Ephemeroptera occur in all habitats, both silted and unsilted, though the actual species found in each habitat vary considerably. Hemiptera, on the other hand, are entirely confined to habitats where the current is very slow, being abundant only where large amounts of silt are present. Trichoptera, which are rarely abundant in the lower reaches, are commoner as a group in the more silted habitats, whilst Diptera are very numerous everywhere, though different species are characteristic of each biotope. Coleoptera are common in all habitats except the more silted ones; this is mainly because most of the specimens found are Elmidae which are crawling forms, and as such require a firm substrate. Mollusca occur commonly in most habitats except silted gravel at the edge of pools—their absence here possibly being due to the fact that this is the only substrate which dries up regularly at low water levels (cf. Hunter, 1953).

The habitats of weed, stones and riffle are the only ones which are common in all parts of the River Endrick. It is, moreover, only weed and stones in current which occur above the lower reaches—as well as, of course, riffle, in which current is a basic feature. The main characteristics of the fauna of these three habitats in the lower reaches have already been discussed. Whilst the habitats of stones and riffle are basically similar in all parts of the river, the species of weed occurring in various reaches are different—thus *Potamogeton* and *Myriophyllum* are common in the lower reaches, *Myriophyllum* and *Fontinalis* in the middle reaches, and *Fontinalis* and other aquatic mosses in the upper reaches. These differences must be borne in mind when comparing the different invertebrate communities found among these weeds.

The composition of the fauna of weed, stones and riffle in different reaches of the river is given in Table 3, from which it can be seen that Coelenterata, Platyhelminthes, Odonata, Hemiptera, Neuroptera, Lepidoptera and Hydracarina are all uncommon or absent in

Table 3.—Percentage composition of the invertebrate fauna of the main biotopes found in the lower (I), middle (II) and upper (III) reaches of the river

Invertebrate Fauna	Weed			Stone			Riffle		
	I	II	III	I	II	III	I	II	III
Coelenterata	0·1	—	—	—	—	—	0·1	—	—
Platyhelminthes	0·1	0·7	—	0·1	—	—	0·1	0·3	0·6
Oligochaeta	10·0	0·6	6·8	5·6	0·5	1·8	16·2	4·1	1·1
Hirudinea	0·7	—	—	0·1	0·1	—	5·6	0·1	—
Crustacea	6·0	0·5	—	7·6	0·2	—	3·8	0·5	0·5
Ephemeroptera	7·4	23·6	4·3	12·1	3·2	4·0	12·4	21·3	18·7
Plecoptera	0·4	32·6	41·9	1·2	2·7	17·8	1·9	18·5	47·0
Odonata	—	—	—	—	—	—	—	—	—
Hemiptera	—	—	—	—	—	—	—	—	—
Neuroptera	—	0·1	—	—	—	—	—	0·1	0·1
Trichoptera	0·4	15·7	3·7	0·6	34·6	25·7	0·4	11·1	8·5
Lepidoptera	—	—	—	—	—	—	—	—	—
Diptera	59·8	20·7	38·0	58·1	35·4	28·2	39·2	32·7	18·5
Coleoptera	3·6	4·8	4·9	7·6	4·7	7·1	11·4	9·5	4·7
Hydracarina	2·2	0·4	0·1	0·9	1·0	—	0·3	0·5	0·1
Mollusca	9·3	0·3	0·3	6·1	17·6	15·4	8·6	1·3	0·2
No. Samples	6	9	6	3	9	3	9	12	9
Ave. No. Sample	1888	884	405	1266	896	359	1312	1672	710

these habitats throughout the main river. Oligochaeta occur in all three habitats in all reaches, but are more abundant in the lower parts of the river; this abundance may be related to the more silted nature of this stretch as a whole. Hirudinea are always absent from the upper reaches and uncommon in the middle reaches, whilst in the lower reaches they are common only in riffle. Crustacea too, are common only in the lower reaches, whilst Ephemeroptera occur in considerable numbers in all three habitats throughout the river. Plecoptera, however, are never abundant in the lower reaches of the river, but in the middle and upper reaches—especially the latter—they are one of the most important constituents of the fauna in all habitats. Neither are Trichoptera abundant in the lower river, but they too are of great importance further upstream, particularly in the middle reaches. Diptera are abundant everywhere, whilst Coleoptera too, occur commonly in all three habitats in all reaches.

As mentioned above, riffle is one of the commonest habitats above the extreme lower reaches of the river, and Table 4 gives the composition of this habitat at ten stations, from Drymen to the source.

Table 4.—Percentage composition of the invertebrate fauna of riffle at stations 3 to 12 in the River Endrick

Fauna	3	4	5	6	7	8	9	10	11	12
Coelenterata	0·1	—	0·1	—	—	—	—	—	—	—
Platyhelminthes	0·1	0·1	0·1	0·1	0·1	0·1	1·0	1·9	—	—
Oligochaeta	4·5	27·9	7·8	11·5	3·1	1·3	0·5	0·7	0·3	2·1
Hirudinea	0·1	11·1	0·2	0·1	—	—	—	—	—	—
Crustacea	6·4	1·2	0·7	0·9	0·8	0·2	0·1	1·8	—	—
Ephemeroptera	14·4	10·4	24·0	22·0	18·4	24·4	20·4	26·7	9·4	20·1
Plecoptera	3·1	0·8	3·8	3·9	8·4	24·8	27·0	37·4	56·4	46·7
Odonata	—	—	—	—	—	—	—	—	—	—
Hemiptera	—	—	—	—	—	—	—	—	—	—
Neuroptera	—	—	—	—	—	0·1	—	—	—	0·4
Trichoptera	0·4	0·5	3·1	3·9	20·4	11·1	19·0	8·7	8·8	7·9
Lepidoptera	—	—	—	—	—	—	—	—	—	—
Diptera	53·1	25·2	38·5	42·0	32·8	27·9	28·3	18·2	20·0	17·3
Coleoptera	10·9	11·8	14·5	13·6	11·5	9·5	3·4	3·9	4·8	5·5
Hydracarina	0·5	0·1	0·8	1·6	0·1	0·4	0·1	0·1	0·2	—
Mollusca	6·4	10·9	6·4	0·4	4·4	0·2	0·2	0·6	0·1	—
No. Samples	6	3	3	3	3	3	3	3	3	3
Ave. No. Sample	1663	1834	1116	2522	1373	1497	1296	864	741	524

The substrate concerned is basically similar at most of these stations —station 4 (Dalnair), however, should be regarded with caution, for it is affected by mild organic pollution from the Blane Water (Maitland, 1962*b*). This accounts for the high numbers of Oligochaeta and Hirudinea and the low numbers of Plecoptera found there. In general, Coelenterata, Platyhelminthes, Hirudinea, Odonata, Hemiptera, Neuroptera, Lepidoptera and Hydracarina are uncommon or absent in this habitat throughout the river. Oligochaeta, Crustacea, Diptera, Coleoptera and Mollusca show a tendency to decrease in importance from mouth to source, whilst the reverse is true of Plecoptera. Ephemeroptera and Trichoptera are most important in the middle reaches.

Distribution

It can be seen from the foregoing, that in many habitats in the River Endrick the same groups are of importance, these being Oligochaeta, Crustacea, Ephemeroptera, Plecoptera, Trichoptera, Diptera, Coleoptera and Mollusca. Numerically, these animals make up the bulk of the fauna in almost every habitat, except in the lower reaches where Hemiptera are important in still water. In any one stretch, most of the variations between the fauna of various habitats can be related directly to the obvious differences between these habitats (e.g. the substrates), as has previously been noted by Moon (1938). The degree of silting is evidently a very important factor in determining the composition of the invertebrate community, but is not an easy one to analyze accurately. Both it and the nature of the substrate itself are in most cases directly dependent on the speed of the current, as is discussed above.

When dealing with the fauna at group level, it must be emphasized that certain similarities or differences which are apparent between particular groups in different habitats may be artificial ones, for different species of these groups may be involved in each case. This matter is more fully discussed below in dealing with zonation, where the distribution of individual species is examined more closely. One of the most outstanding features of the present general analysis of the population composition in various habitats is that the communities of different substrates in the same reach of the river may tend to resemble each other more closely than those of the same substrates in different reaches. This can be seen from some of the figures in Table 3, and appears to be particularly true for groups like Crustacea and Plecoptera. It would suggest that, to such groups, the physical and chemical conditions of the environment are more important than the actual nature of the substrate—though obviously this will be true only within certain limits.

The same situation is even more apparent when dealing with the distribution of the fauna at specific level. Thus most species of Oligochaeta, Crustacea, Hirudinea and Mollusca are much more common in all substrates in the lower reaches than in any other parts of the river; undoubtedly much of this is due to overflow of the populations of the species concerned from their optimum habitat into the others. Likewise, most species of Ephemeroptera, Plecoptera and Trichoptera are much more common in the middle and upper reaches, irrespective of substrate, than anywhere in the lower reaches. Such results might provide some justification for dividing the River Endrick into zones at group level, were it not for the fact that in each group there are usually one or more species which have a distribution opposite to the majority. Examples from the River Endrick of the above groups in which this is the case include *Eiseniella tetraedra* (Oligochaeta), *Gammarus pulex* (Crustacea), *Centroptilum luteolum* (Ephemeroptera), *Agraylea multipunctata* (Trichoptera) and *Ancylus fluviatilis* (Mollusca), the subject being discussed more fully below.

IV. QUANTITATIVE STUDIES ON INVERTEBRATES

Most of the first faunistic studies of running waters originated in Europe and were concerned with qualitative aspects of mountain streams (Steinmann, 1907; Thienneman, 1912). Many of the accounts which followed these were of a similar nature (e.g. Carpenter, 1927; Eidel, 1933; Nietzke, 1938; and Jones, 1941). Behning (1924) was probably the first person to produce an analysis of the fauna of a lowland river (the Volga), and this study included some useful quantitative data. In America, Richardson (1921 and 1929) carried out a classical study of the Illinois River, and later this was followed by many other accounts, some of them concerned with practical fishery investigations (e.g. Ludwig, 1932; Ide, 1940; and Idyll, 1943). Many of the most useful recent studies have come from Europe (Berg, 1948; Illies, 1952, 1953; Albrecht, 1953; and Dittmar, 1955) and Africa (Harrison and Elsworth, 1958; and Oliff, 1960), and have contained useful quantitative information.

Several faunistic studies of running waters have been carried out in Great Britain, but as already mentioned there are few data for Scotland to compare with the research carried out in Wales by Carpenter (1927); Jones (1940, etc.); Badcock (1949) and Hynes (1961); in England by Percival and Whitehead (1929 and 1930); Butcher, Pentelow and Woodley (1930); Whitehead (1935); Butcher, Longwell and Pentelow (1937) and Moon (1937, etc.). Formerly the only accounts of the fauna of any rivers in Scotland were those of Neill (1938) and Allen (1941)—both of these being subsidiary to feeding studies of fish—but recently several other accounts have been published (Maitland, 1962b, 1964a; Egglishaw, 1964; Mills, 1964; Morgan and Egglishaw, 1965), thus considerably extending knowledge of the ecology of rivers in this country.

Many difficulties are involved in the quantitative sampling of stream faunas. The varied nature of the substrate in different streams and even from place to place within one stream means that more than one type of sampler may have to be used. In the River Endrick the substrate ranges from fine mud, through sand, gravel and stones to boulders and solid rock; in the present study several different methods were used. This inevitably gives rise to difficulty of comparison of the results, and here only general conclusions have been drawn from the data available. Wherever possible, methods of washing, sieving and sorting were standardized to minimize this difficulty. The data for two of the stations described below (Woodend and Drumtian) have been published in detail elsewhere (Maitland, 1964*a*) and only a limited amount of this is presented below for comparative purposes, together with new data.

The Habitats Studied

Three stretches of the River Endrick were studied regularly on a quantitative or semi-quantitative basis. These were selected initially to include the most important types of substrate occurring in the river and comprised station A (Woodend) in the lower reaches, station B (Drumtian) in the middle reaches, and station C (Altquhur) on one of the tributary streams entering the main river (Fig. 1). Occasional quantitative samples were taken at other places, e.g. in connection with the pollution studies described below.

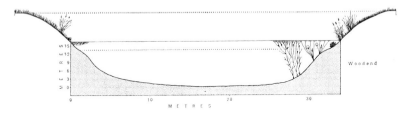

Fig. 5A.—A transverse section of the River Endrick at station A
(Woodend)

At station A (Woodend) the substrate is sandy with a little detritus and this represents over 80 per cent of the river bed in the lower reaches. The stretch studied occurs in the middle part of the lower reaches and is some 100 m. long, the average depth being about 1·5 m. and the breadth 35 m. (Fig. 5A). The river current here is normally very slow. A few Alders are found along the banks of the river at this point and the fields on either side are mostly used for rough pasture. No macrophytes grow in the middle of the river here, but at the edge *Potamogeton natans, Potamogeton crispus, Elodea canadensis, Polygonum amphibium* and *Nuphar lutea* are common. Vegetation growing near the edge of the water consists of a variety of plants among which *Juncus effusus* and *Phalaris arundinacea* are common. These are submerged, often for long periods, during high water in winter, and offer cover to certain invertebrates and fish at this time. The banks of the river here are unstable in certain places and

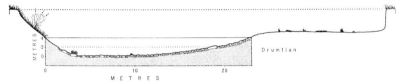

Fig. 5B.—A transverse section of the River Endrick at station B
(Drumtian)

often large sections are washed away during spates. Roach, Pike and Perch are the most common fish species found in this stretch.

At station B (Drumtian) the substrate consists mainly of small stones and gravel, though occasional larger stones are present also; this substrate represents over 60 per cent of the river bed in the middle reaches. The stretch studied in detail is in the lower part of the middle reaches and is some 200 m. long, the average depth being less than 0·5 m. and the breadth 20 m. (Fig. 5B). The current here is normally fast. There is a small wood on the left bank—mostly Alder —whilst open fields lie on the right bank, these normally being used for pasture, though occasionally they are ploughed for crops. *Fontinalis antipyretica* grows on some of the more stable stones in the river bed here and there are also patches of *Myriophyllum alterniflorum* near the left bank. Most of the river banks here are unstable and their erosion is facilitated in some places by the activities of cattle and sheep, these disturbing the soil, much of which is washed away by the next spate thus severely undercutting the bank at these points. The common fish species at Drumtian are Salmon, Trout, Minnow, Stone Loach and Three-spined Stickleback.

At station C (Altquhur) the substrate consists mainly of sand, gravel and small stones, and large clumps of *Myriophyllum alterniflorum* are common. This station is on one of the tributary streams which enters the main river between station A and station B, near the junction of the middle and the lower reaches (Fig. 1). The stretch studied in the Altquhur Burn is about 2 km. long, the average depth being about 20 cm. and the average breadth 3 m. (Fig. 5c). The current in most places is fast. Alders occur very commonly along the banks of the stream at this point, often causing heavy shading. The fields on either side are rough pasture and the banks are for the

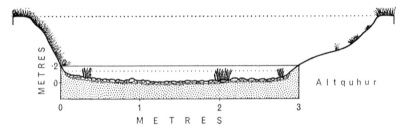

Fig. 5c.—A transverse section of the River Endrick at station C
(Altquhur)

most part stable except where the course of the river curves sharply. Salmon, Trout, Minnow and Stone Loach are the common fish species found in this part of the Altquhur Burn.

All three stations were under observation for three years, from July 1959 to July 1962. Stations A and B were studied intensively from November 1959 to January 1961 and station C from December 1960 to December 1961. Regular observations of temperature, water level, current speed and pH were made at all three stations and water samples were taken for analysis, particularly for calcium and oxygen as described in more detail elsewhere (Maitland, 1964a). Monthly samples of the substrate were taken from the river bed at each station, using a different method in each case but always sampling to a depth of 12 cm. Once in each month 3 samples were taken at station A using a Petersen grab (Heuts, 1946; Weerekoon, 1956; Maitland, 1964a), 3 samples were taken at station B using a modified shovel sampler (Macan, 1958; Maitland, 1964a), and 1 sample was taken at station C using a handnet for a standard period of 10 minutes (Macan, 1957*a*; Hynes, 1961). The samples were taken from the river to the laboratory, where they were washed and sieved, coarse sievings being sorted by eye in shallow dishes, fine sievings being sorted under the low power of a binocular microscope.

As fine a mesh as possible was used when dealing with these quantitative samples, in practice a mesh of 65 threads per cm. being found to be suitable. All the animals in the samples from stations A and B which were retained by this mesh are included in the results given below, but for several reasons (Maitland, 1965) only the animals in samples from station C which were retained by a mesh of 16 threads per cm. are considered below. Thus, though the masses of animals collected at different stations may be comparable (see below), the numbers are not; this difference in method accounts also for the apparent high average weight of the animals at station C compared with those of the animals at stations A and B.

Occasional qualitative samples of the bottom fauna were taken at all three stations at various times of the year by handnet or dredge in order to obtain insects which could be reared for identification purposes. These insects were taken to the laboratory and kept there in small tanks similar to those described by Hynes (1941). Odd samples were also taken at station B with a fine mesh net in order to sample for "organic drift" (Müller, 1954); this appears to be very sparse here except during spates (Maitland, 1964*a*). At station C numerous samples of interstitial water were taken from among gravel beds with the specific object of collecting specimens of *Bathynella natans* (Maitland, 1962*a*).

Jonasson (1955) has shown conclusively that the size of mesh used in dealing with samples of aquatic bottom fauna is of supreme importance where accurate numerical analysis is required, as in quantitative studies. Many workers have ignored this factor; others, whilst mentioning it, very rarely attempt to assess exactly what the loss may be with various mesh sizes. As mentioned elsewhere, each sample of bottom fauna from the Altquhur Burn was washed through a number of sieves, there being five of these, with 4, 16, 23, 39, and 65 meshes per cm. The method adopted in sieving each of these samples was as follows. Each sample was placed in a plastic basin together with some water. The entire contents of this basin were then emptied into a similar basin through the first sieve (4 meshes per cm.) and this sieve was shaken gently up and down in the water in this basin for a standard period of 5 minutes. The washings were then poured through the next sieve in the series into the first basin and the process was repeated. After washing, the material retained in each sieve was sorted and identified.

The results of the analysis of a typical sample are shown in Fig. 6. It can be seen that the numbers of various groups passing through the coarse meshes were considerable, e.g. over 50 per cent of the total fauna passed through the 16 meshes per cm. sieve in this sample. This sample was further analyzed by weighing the different groups found in each fraction: it can be seen that the greater part of the fauna by weight (99 per cent) was retained by the sieve of 16 meshes per cm.

It would be seen from this that where coarse meshes are used in sieving samples of bottom fauna, some estimate of either the loss by number of the animals or the weight retained should be made. For this reason, figures for bulk are used in this study when dealing with data concerning fish feeding and bottom fauna collected by coarse meshes. Moreover, as has been pointed out elsewhere (Maitland, 1964a) it is particularly important where fish food and standing crop are concerned that some idea of the weight of the invertebrates involved should be given—especially for comparative purposes.

Environmental Data

Many more chemical and physical data were obtained for stations A and B than for C and consequently these feature more prominently in the results discussed below. Also, the samples of bottom fauna taken at stations A and B were taken on an area basis and can be compared with each other more readily than with the timed collections from station C. Moreover, most of the collections from stations A and B and station C were taken in different years, and consequently only very general conclusions including all three stations are permissible.

Chemical results indicate that the water near the substrate was

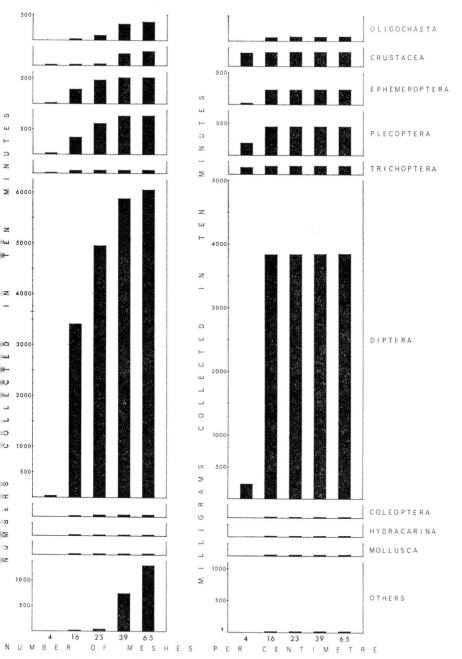

Fig. 6.—The numbers and weights of animals retained by sieves of different meshes in a sample of invertebrate fauna from the Altquhur Burn

81

similar at all three stations, though certain small differences are apparent. Dissolved oxygen was always high (93·7, 96·9 and 98·8 per cent averages at stations A, B and C respectively), the slight differences in average agreeing with the relative turbulence at the three stations. The average pH values recorded at stations A and B were similar (7·3 and 7·5 respectively) but that at station C (6·8) was lower. The average amount of calcium found in the water at station A (18·2 mg./l.) was greater than that at station B (15·9 mg./l.), and both were higher than that at station C (11·2 mg./l.). No record of the magnesium present at station C was obtained, but values of 5·5 mg./l. and 4·4 mg./l. were estimated at stations A and B respectively on the basis of only two analyses at each station.

Detailed weekly chemical analyses of the water at stations A and B are available for the period from the 30th September to the 16th December 1960, and these are given in Table 5. The average amounts of solids present—both suspended and dissolved—were similar at both stations, those at station A (8·8 and 10·8 mg./l. respectively for suspended and dissolved solids) being slightly greater than those at station B (6·7 and 10·2 mg./l.). The same is true of chlorides (as Cl) and various forms of nitrogen. The oxygen demand at station A was normally greater than that at station B, indicating that the water at the former station was richer organically. Much of this may be due to the action of polluting material flowing in to the main river from the Blane Water, which normally carries a greater amount of sewage (see below).

The results obtained for the water current speed at all stations were unsatisfactory. It was hoped to obtain a regular record of the current speed at 10 cm. below the surface in mid-stream: at station A, however, the current was often too slow to give a reading on the current meter being used, and even simple methods, such as timing a float as it passed downstream (Badcock, 1949) were usually impossible because of wind interference. At stations B and C better records of current speed were obtained, but even here gauging was often impossible because of high water. In general it may be said that the current at station A is usually slow (5 to 10 cm./sec.) though speeds of over 40 cm./sec. have been recorded during spates. At station B the current is fast (30 to 50 cm./sec.), but again, much faster

Table 5.—Chemical analyses (in milligrams per litre) of water samples taken from station A (Woodend) and station B (Drumtian) between 30th September and 16th December, 1960

Station A (Woodend)	30/9	7/10	14/10	21/10	28/10	4/11	11/11	18/11	25/11	2/12	9/12	16/12	Ave.
Temperature (°C)	10·5	11·5	7·5	9·5	10·0	7·5	7·0	5·0	5·0	6·0	3·0	2·5	7·0
pH	7·6	7·5	7·4	7·5	7·4	7·2	7·2	7·2	7·2	7·0	7·2	7·3	7·3
Suspended Solids	10	4		14	2	13	14	5	8	18	6	8	9
Dissolved Solids	134	114	123	107	126	95	87	110	91	88	104	115	108
Chloride (as Cl)	9	9	9	8	10	10	10	12	10	7	8	11	9
Alkalinity (as $CaCO_3$)	60	45	55	40	45	30	35	40	25	25	39	55	41
Ammoniacal Nitrogen	nil	trace	nil	nil	nil	nil	nil	nil	nil	nil	nil	nil	nil
Albuminoid Nitrogen	0·07	0·08	0·01	0·10	0·10	0·25	0·07	0·10	0·15	0·13	0·82	0·08	0·16
Nitrous Nitrogen	0·01	0·01	0·01	0·02	0·01	0·01	nil	0·01	nil	trace	0·01	0·01	0·01
Nitric Nitrogen	0·14	nil	trace	0·10	nil	nil	trace	0·16	nil	0·10	trace	0·14	0·0
Dissolved Oxygen	10·6	9·5	11·1	10·2	9·9	10·9	10·8	11·5	11·5	11·3	12·2	13·3	11·1
% Sat. Diss. Oxygen	97·7	90·1	95·0	92·3	90·7	93·8	91·8	93·0	93·0	93·3	93·5	100·2	93·7
B.O.D.	1·4	1·3	1·5	1·4	1·3	1·4	1·6	1·6	1·8	1·2	2·4	2·5	1·6
O_2 absorbed from $KMnO_4$ in 4 hours	4·1	5·0	3·7	9·5	5·9	9·7	9·3	6·1	9·8	6·7	3·9	3·5	6·4
River Level (cm.)	148	158	145	155	154	177	195	190	199	236	189	207	179
Station B (Drumtian)													
Temperature (°C)	9·0	10·5	6·5	9·5	9·5	7·0	7·0	4·5	4·5	5·0	3·0	4·0	7·0
pH	7·6	7·5	7·5	7·5	7·4	7·2	7·2	7·2	7·2	7·1	7·3	7·2	7·3
Suspended Solids	6	2	4	2	5	12	16	6	9	13	3	2	7
Dissolved Solids	126	104	126	111	103	97	92	102	84	81	93	109	102
Chloride (as Cl)	8	8	9	8	10	10	11	12	9	6	7	10	9
Alkalinity (as $CaCO_3$)	65	45	60	40	45	30	30	40	25	30	38	45	41
Ammoniacal Nitrogen	nil	nil	nil	nil	nil	nil	nil	nil	nil	nil	nil	nil	nil
Albuminoid Nitrogen	0·05	0·08	0·01	0·08	0·13	0·27	0·08	0·10	0·10	0·10	0·82	0·11	0·16
Nitrous Nitrogen	0·01	0·01	0·01	0·02	0·01	0·01	nil	0·01	nil	0·12	trace	0·12	0·03
Nitric Nitrogen	0·12	nil	trace	0·16	nil	nil	trace	0·12	nil	0·12	trace	0·12	0·05
Dissolved Oxygen	11·4	10·4	12·3	10·6	10·9	11·3	11·1	12·2	12·1	11·6	12·6	13·0	11·6
% Sat. Diss. Oxygen	101·9	96·5	103·3	95·9	98·6	96·1	94·4	97·3	96·5	93·4	96·6	102·3	97·7
B.O.D.	1·3	1·0	1·6	1·1	1·4	1·4	2·0	1·6	2·0	1·2	1·8	2·8	1·6
O_2 absorbed from $KMnO_4$ in 4 hours	3·5	2·8	2·5	6·6	6·9	7·4	8·6	5·1	6·5	4·3	3·1	1·8	4·9
River Level (cm.)	22	25	25	44	52	61	94	66	54	70	43	41	50

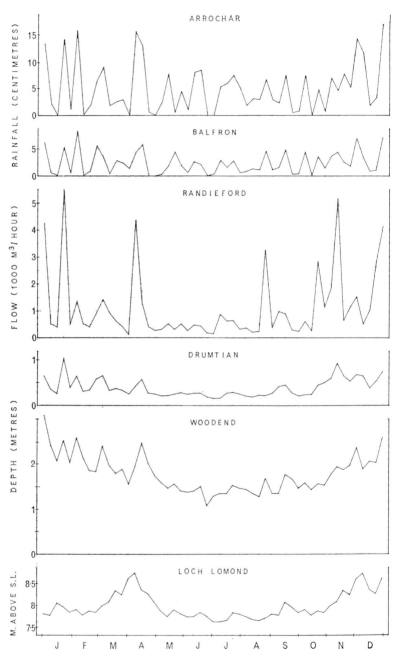

Fig. 7.—The weekly rainfall at Arrochar and Balfron, the flow at Randieford, the depth at Drumtian and Woodend and the height above sea-level of Loch Lomond, during 1960

speeds have been recorded during spates (over 150 cm./sec. on one occasion). At station C too the current is fast (25 to 40 cm./sec.), and here also much faster speeds have been recorded during spates.

The water levels at stations A and B were recorded only once each week during 1960, but several factors of interest can be noted from these readings, especially when they are compared with other data available for the area in the same year (Fig. 7). The fluctuation in level was considerable at both stations, about 2 m. at station A where the average depth was 1·61 m. and over 0·75 m. at station B where the average depth was 0·39 m. In general, the fluctuations at station A in the lower reaches were similar to those at station B in the middle reaches, and high levels at both these places corresponded to peak flows at Randieford in the upper reaches (see also Fig. 19). These are all associated directly with the rainfall during the previous week, which is considerably greater in the highland part of the Loch Lomond area (e.g. near Arrochar at 213 m. above sea-level, where the average rainfall for 1960 was 261·6 cm.), than in the lowland part (e.g. near Balfron at 65 m. above sea-level, where the average rainfall for 1960 was 124·3 cm.). The level of the water in Loch Lomond, though related to the rainfall in the area, does not follow it so directly as do the river levels. Also, the loch level is much more stable and is rarely subject to the sharp rises and falls which are characteristic of the River Endrick.

Water level readings at station C were taken only infrequently during 1961. They followed a similar pattern to those recorded at stations A and B at the same time, though the Altquhur Burn appears to be less drastically affected by spates than much of the rest of the river system—possibly due to the stabilizing effect of Muirpark Reservoir (Fig. 2) in its upper reaches (McLean, 1940).

The water temperatures recorded during 1960 at stations A and B are shown in Fig. 8 together with the air temperatures recorded at the level of Loch Lomond (Tarbet) during the same period. The maximum temperatures at stations A and B during this time were 22°C. and 24°C. respectively, both considerably lower than the maximum air temperature at Tarbet of 31°C. Minimum temperatures of 0°C. were recorded on several occasions at both station A and station B, but whilst ice cover formed quite frequently at station A

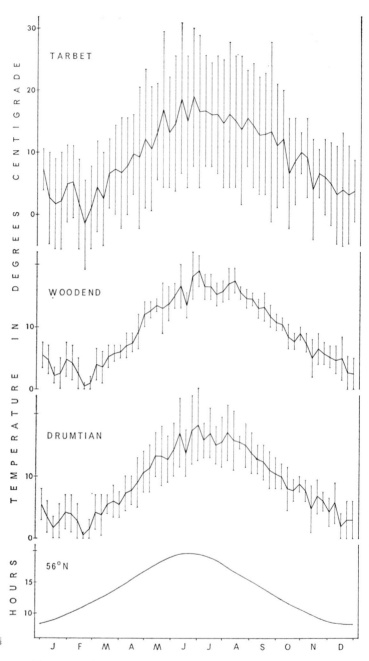

Fig. 8.—Weekly records of the maximum and minimum air temperatures at Tarbet and water temperatures at Woodend (station A) and Drumtian (station B). The daylength at 56°N. is also included

where the current was slow, this was never the case at station B, where the current was fast—ice forming here only at the edges around stones. The minimum air temperature recorded at Tarbet during 1960 was −8·8°C.

In general, the pattern of the weekly temperatures during 1960 was similar at all places. The average weekly temperature of the water at station A tended always to be closer to that of the previous week than that at station B, whilst the fluctuations at station B were always greater than those at station A—though never so great as the air temperatures at Tarbet. These differences in temperature stability between the middle and lower reaches of the River Endrick are clearly directly related to the nature of the river in each stretch: at station B the current is fast and turbulent and the river is shallow, allowing intimate contact of water with air. Consequently the water temperature here follows the air temperature much more rapidly than that at station A, where the current is slow and the river deep.

Species Present

The general composition of the invertebrate fauna at these three stations can be seen in Table 6. Crustacea and Diptera were important groups at all three stations, whilst Oligochaeta and Mollusca were important also at stations A and B, as were Ephemeroptera and Coleoptera at stations B and C. At all stations the maxima both of number and weight per unit area occurred during the summer and the minima during the winter (Fig. 9).

At station A the Coelenterata were all *Hydra vulgaris*. Common Oligochaeta were *Stylaria lacustris*, *Nais pseudobtusa*, *Limnodrilus longus*, *Rhyacodrilus coccineus* and *Tubifex ignota*, whilst less common species were *Ripistes parasita*, *Aulodrilus pluriseta* and *Stilodrilus heringianus*. Hirudinea were very uncommon, though both *Glossiphonia complanata* and *Erpobdella octoculata* occurred at times. Of the Crustacea, *Alona affinis*, *Cyclops fuscus* and *Cyclops viridis* were common, whilst *Sida crystallina*, *Eurycercus lamellatus*, *Asellus aquaticus* and unidentified Ostracoda were also recorded. Ephemeroptera were uncommon, only *Caenis macrura*, *Ephemerella ignita* and *Centroptilum luteolum* being recorded, whilst the only member of the

Table 6.—The density per square metre of the invertebrate fauna at station A (Woodend) and station B (Drumtian) in 1960, and the numbers of invertebrates collected per 10 minutes at station C (Altquhur) in 1961

Fauna	J	F	M	A	M	J	J	A	S	O	N	D
WOODEND												
Coelenterata	—	—	—	—	—	36	171	108	—	—	—	—
Oligochaeta	3575	4055	4694	2442	6902	19353	9506	8280	5226	6965	5388	1919
Hirudinea	—	—	18	—	—	—	27	—	—	—	—	9
Crustacea	27	18	36	18	9	252	2532	16813	36	18	45	27
Ephemeroptera	—	—	—	—	—	63	45	27	—	—	—	9
Plecoptera	—	—	—	—	—	—	—	—	—	—	—	9
Trichoptera	—	—	—	—	—	—	—	—	—	—	—	—
Diptera	937	721	1964	667	604	22174	27192	12650	369	1117	964	288
Coleoptera	18	9	9	9	18	18	63	54	9	—	27	—
Hydracarina	198	72	9	—	—	—	27	27	—	—	27	—
Mollusca	117	135	117	198	108	847	874	1207	153	54	36	45
Others	—	—	180	162	550	505	622	414	—	90	90	108
Total	4872	5010	7027	3496	8191	43248	41059	39580	5793	8244	6577	2414
DRUMTIAN												
Coelenterata	—	—	—	—	—	103	2525	13554	725	1546	91	—
Oligochaeta	259	834	501	2356	4143	3774	2150	7407	4034	2738	2338	839
Hirudinea	18	30	18	12	91	652	284	260	85	91	181	36
Crustacea	18	18	30	103	429	1438	211	1625	1190	193	749	97

Ephemeroptera	489	755	2537	1160	3243	13469	6650	8565	224	362	151	85
Plecoptera	60	139	139	91	24	266	447	314	85	54	103	79
Trichoptera	139	115	260	127	405	447	390	368	6	18	79	85
Diptera	33087	37925	61614	25807	79523	48465	56130	48423	8637	9869	37907	31752
Coleoptera	290	864	1540	2676	3165	1105	749	1015	1142	24	948	217
Hydracarina	332	217	1172	834	1697	707	616	870	60	91	157	260
Mollusca	211	181	683	737	4784	3213	7097	1444	477	205	2132	2929
Others	308	658	749	308	1425	374	713	3195	2513	374	827	60
Total	35888	44213	73262	37774	117112	73216	78759	68857	15615	11546	43186	35762

ALTQUHUR

Coelenterata	—	—	—	—	—	1	—	—	—	—	—	—
Oligochaeta	25	99	5	50	35	153	380	245	167	151	93	23
Hirudinea	—	—	—	—	—	1	—	—	—	1	—	—
Crustacea	25	58	46	131	71	122	155	125	61	17	24	16
Ephemeroptera	574	599	615	359	1000	2166	1799	859	646	852	240	282
Plecoptera	160	264	88	81	167	179	1021	470	434	635	352	333
Trichoptera	35	40	49	20	47	6	27	127	87	85	90	54
Diptera	772	761	380	116	1701	2253	3008	2954	382	850	1229	3411
Coleoptera	28	77	96	107	320	226	331	120	216	227	135	23
Hydracarina	25	58	46	131	71	122	155	125	61	17	22	2
Mollusca	9	4	11	11	2	4	—	4	6	1	9	5
Others	5	56	58	14	16	10	119	24	113	110	56	41
Total	1658	2016	1394	1020	3430	5243	6995	5053	2173	2946	2250	4190

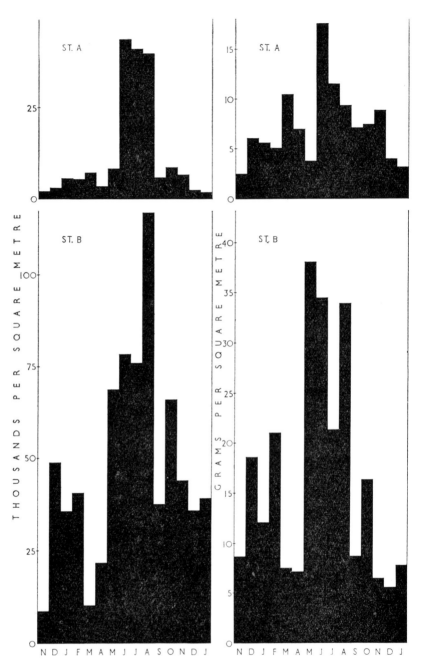

Fig. 9a.—The monthly densities and weights per square metre of the total invertebrate populations at station A (Woodend) and station B (Drumtian) from November 1959 to January 1961

90

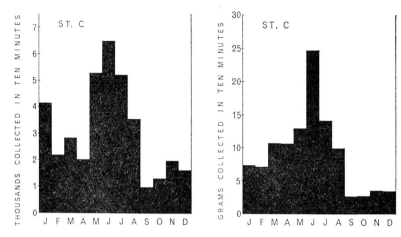

Fig. 9B.—The monthly numbers and weights of invertebrate animals collected in 10 minutes from the substrate at station C (Altquhur) from January 1961 to December 1961

Plecoptera found was a single specimen of *Leuctra hippopus*. No Trichoptera were taken but Diptera larvae were very common, especially Chironomidae—the genera *Pentaneura, Procladius, Chironomus, Stictochironomus, Tanytarsus, Prodiamesa* and *Orthocladius* being predominant. Other Chironomidae recorded were *Pentapedilum, Polypedilum, Microtendipes, Diamesa, Cricotopus* and *Corynoneura*; the exact species to which some of these larvae may be referred are discussed above. Other Diptera recorded were *Bezzia, Culicoides, Hemerodromia* and *Simulium,* but only the first of these was ever common. The few Coleoptera collected were all larval Elmidae, mostly *Latelmis volkmari,* though *Helmis maugei, Limnius tuberculatus* and *Esolus parallelopipedus* were also recorded. Hydracarina were always uncommon, and the only adult found was *Hygrobates fluviatilis.* Mollusca were almost all Sphaeriidae, especially common species being *Pisidium amnicum, P. subtruncatum* and *P. henslowanum,* though *Planorbis albus* was also recorded on one occasion. Other animals found were mostly unidentified Nematoda.

The characteristic features of this fauna in the River Endrick are similar to those of the fauna in sandy substrates which have been studied elsewhere in the world. Thus Behning (1924) showed that in

7

this substrate in the River Volga the main components of the fauna were all burrowing forms, mainly Oligochaeta (*Limnodrilus* being the dominant form), Chironomidae (*Tanypus*, *Chironomus* and *Sticto-chironomus*) and Sphaeriidae (*Sphaerium* and *Pisidium*). In the River Susaa at the Meanders, Berg (1948) found a similar community (though a somewhat richer one), Oligochaeta, Chironomidae and Sphaeriidae again being the dominant groups. In the profundal region of Loch Lomond, Weerekoon (1956) noted that these three groups were also the dominant forms.

At station B the Coelenterata were again all *Hydra vulgaris*. Common species of Oligochaeta were *Nais pseudobtusa*, *Pristina foreli*, *Limnodrilus longus*, *Rhyacodrilus coccineus* and *Lumbriculus variegatus*, whilst other species taken included *Chaetogaster cristallinus*, *Stylaria lacustris*, *Peloscolex ferox*, *Stilodrilus heringianus* and unidentified Enchytraeidae. Of the Hirudinea, *Glossiphonia complanata* and *Helob-della stagnalis* were common, whilst *Dina lineata* was recorded on one occasion. Crustacea were represented by *Gammarus pulex* (which was never abundant), *Alona affinis* and species of *Cyclops*, Harpacticoidea and Ostracoda. Several Ephemeroptera were common, *Caenis rivu-lorum*, *Ephemerella ignita*, *Ecdyonurus venosus*, *Rhithrogena semi-colorata* and *Baetis rhodani* being at times abundant. Other species recorded were *Ecdyonurus insignis* and *Baetis pumilus*. Several species of Plecoptera were recorded—*Brachyptera risi*, *Amphinemura sulci-collis*, *Leuctra geniculata*, *L. inermis*, *L. hippopus*, *L. fusca*, *Isoperla grammatica* and *Chloroperla torrentium*—but, rather surprisingly perhaps, few of these were ever common. Common species of Trichoptera were *Hydropsyche instabilis*, *Polycentropus flavomaculatus* and *Rhyacophila dorsalis*. *Potamophylax* sp., *Agapetus fuscipes*, *Psychomyia pusilla* and *Hydroptila* sp. were also found. As at station A the Diptera larvae were mostly Chironomidae, and here the genera *Tanytarsus*, *Orthocladius*, *Eukiefferiella* and *Corynoneura* were ex-tremely abundant, whilst *Pentaneura*, *Stictochironomus*, *Pentapedilum*, *Cardiocladius* and *Trichocladius* were also recorded. Various other Diptera larvae were found including *Tipula*, *Dicranota*, and *Hemero-dromia*; whilst Simuliidae were sometimes abundant—*Simulium equinum*, *S. ornatum*, *S. reptans* (including its variety *galeratum*) and *S. aureum* all being recorded. Most of the Coleoptera were Elmidae, the larvae and adults of *Helmis maugei, Esolus parallelopipedus* and *Latelmis volkmari* all being common. *Limnius tuberculatus* was less common, and some unidentified larvae of Dytiscidae were also found occasionally. The Hydracarina taken were mostly unidentified larvae, but among the few adults *Lebertia porosa, Torrenticola elliptica, Hygrobates fluviatilis* and *Mideopsis orbicularis* were identified. The Mollusca found were almost all *Ancylus fluviatilis* which was usually common. As at station A, the other animals recorded were mostly unidentified Nematoda, but the Platyhelminthes *Dendrocoelum lacteum* and *Polycelis felina* were also recorded.

At station C (Table 7), as at the other two stations, the only Coelenterata recorded were *Hydra vulgaris*, but this species was not common here. *Nais pseudobtusa, Rhyacodrilus coccineus* and *Lumbriculus variegatus* were the most abundant Oligochaeta though *Chaetogaster crystallinus, Limnodrilus longus* and *Eiseniella tetraedra* were also recorded. Hirudinea were found on only one or two occasions, *Theromyzon tessulatum* and *Helobdella stagnalis* being the only species collected. *Gammarus pulex* was a common member of the Crustacea, but *Cyclops* spp., *Canthocamptus* sp., and *Alona affinis* also occurred, as well as *Bathynella natans*, which is discussed more fully elsewhere (Maitland, 1962a). Of the Ephemeroptera *Ephemerella ignita* and *Baetis rhodani* were at times abundant and *Caenis rivulorum, Ecdyonurus torrentis, Rhithrogena semicolorata, Heptagenia lateralis, Habrophlebia fusca, Leptophlebia marginata, Centroptilum luteolum* and *Baetis pumilus* were also found to be present. Various Plecoptera were also common, *Taeniopteryx nebulosa, Brachyptera risi, Protonemura meyeri, Amphinemura sulcicollis, Nemoura cambrica, Leuctra geniculata, L. inermis, L. hippopus, L. fusca, Capnia bifrons, Isoperla grammatica* and *Chloroperla torrentium* all being recorded. The most common Trichoptera were *Anabolia nervosa, Hydropsyche instabilis, Polycentropus flavomaculatus, Rhyacophila dorsalis* and *Hydroptila forcipata*, but none of these was ever abundant; *Potamophylax stellatus, Beraea maurus, Athripsodes bilineata* and *Agapetus fuscipes* were also recorded. As at stations A and B, Diptera were abundant in the substrate studied in the Altquhur Burn. Five species of Simuliidae were found here: *Simulium equinum, S. ornatum, S. latipes, S. monticola* and *S. variegatum*, the first three of these being the most

Table 7 —The numbers of invertebrate species collected in 10 minutes in the Altquhur Burn in each month in 1961

Fauna	Jan	Feb	Mar	Apr	May	Jun	Jul	Aug	Sep	Oct	Nov	Dec
Naididae	1	7	55	38	24	336	69	4	8	—	85	13
Tubificidae	—	15	8	47	152	7	7	7	26	—	1	1
Lumbriculidae	18	66	74	67	47	42	71	23	16	5	7	6
Enchytraeidae	4	5	10	15	11	—	6	1	—	—	5	5
Caenis rivulorum	1	3	7	4	21	23	3	—	2	—	—	—
Ephemerella ignita	—	—	—	11	422	994	905	102	1	—	—	—
Ecdyonurus torrentis	2	8	3	26	11	127	56	16	—	—	—	—
Rhithrogena semicolorata	3	2	25	18	7	4	—	2	—	—	—	—
Baetis rhodani	270	217	817	576	368	600	1193	878	352	616	597	573
Taeniopteryx nebulosa	3	—	—	—	18	10	6	12	13	13	3	5
Brachyptera risi	73	17	80	5	1	—	—	—	—	—	20	33
Protonemura meyeri	3	3	32	—	—	2	43	88	5	3	5	2
Amphinemura sulcicollis	147	205	237	221	85	—	—	6	51	102	184	111
Nemoura cambrica	22	5	—	1	—	—	—	7	11	3	3	3
Leuctra spp.	33	45	218	140	304	900	129	53	1	4	1	2
Capnia bifrons	40	33	4	1	—	—	—	—	—	—	—	2
Isoperla grammatica	8	35	65	42	43	5	—	1	—	—	44	2
Chloroperla torrentium	4	9	31	28	19	4	1	—	—	2	—	—
Anabolia nervosa	45	64	15	21	11	3	2	4	3	29	3	26
Hydropsyche instabilis	5	18	40	44	14	4	1	32	17	19	21	11
Rhyacophila dorsalis	3	4	14	10	18	17	3	6	—	1	25	2
Hydroptila forcipata	—	—	—	—	71	3	—	—	—	—	3	—
Simulium spp.	3241	931	351	11	25	1686	483	790	43	185	683	651
Dicranota sp.	40	73	179	65	71	424	225	193	16	9	55	13
Tanypodinae	—	6	3	3	14	41	41	—	2	3	5	—
Chironominae	5	41	37	78	66	926	643	153	22	6	12	7
Orthocladiinae	114	161	239	194	2777	168	904	625	56	186	69	84
Helmis maugei	8	58	109	58	54	79	70	115	27	34	25	11
Esolus parallelopipedus	4	14	36	26	21	151	56	27	25	38	22	6
Limnius tuberculatus	11	43	58	66	35	39	73	94	51	3	19	9
Latelmis volkmari	—	19	13	62	9	41	19	25	3	10	10	2
Hydraena gracilis	—	—	2	5	2	1	8	5	1	1	1	—
Hydracarina	2	22	31	34	67	15	61	56	104	25	18	6
Ancylus fluviatilis	—	8	—	3	—	—	1	2	1	1	1	2
Pisidium casertanum	5	1	1	3	3	—	3	—	11	10	3	7
Nematoda	—	2	99	117	92	8	4	10	—	1	—	—
Others	62	86	65	72	46	19	37	15	24	42	29	40
Total	4190	2250	2946	2173	5053	6995	5243	3430	1020	1394	2016	1658

abundant. Other abundant Diptera were *Dicranota*, *Tanytarsus*, *Orthocladius* and *Eukiefferiella*; less common forms were *Tipula*, *Limnophora*, *Hemerodromia*, *Pericoma*, *Dixa*, *Bezzia*, *Pentaneura*, *Procladius*, *Stictochironomus*, *Microtendipes*, *Prodiamesa*, *Smittia*, *Cricotopus*, *Trichocladius* and *Cardiocladius*. As at station B, Elmidae were the most common Coleoptera, *Helmis maugei*, *Esolus parallelo-pipedus*, *Limnius tuberculatus* and *Latelmis volkmari* all being common. Other Coleoptera also recorded were *Graptodytes sanmarki*, *Platambus maculatus*, *Hydraena gracilis*, *Helophorus granularis*, *Anacaena limbata* and *Hydrocyphon deflexicollis*. Only two species of Hydracarina were collected as adults: *Lebertia porosa* and *Hygrobates fluviatilis*; whilst the three species of Mollusca occurring here—*Ancylus fluviatilis*, *Lymnaea pereger* and *Pisidium casertanum*—were all uncommon. Other species of invertebrate found included unidentified Nematoda, *Polycelis felina* and *Sialis fuliginosa*.

The substrates and other environmental features are much more similar at stations B and C than at either of these and station A. The invertebrate faunas at stations B and C show a corresponding similarity and these two stations have, therefore, more species in common than has either with station A. The composition of this fauna is similar to that of other stony substrates in streams which have been studied in Europe, though in certain cases there are differences, notably in the presence or absence of various important species. Thus in the River Braan in Sweden (Badcock, 1953*a*) *Gammarus*, *Ephemerella* and *Baetis* are common, but *Amphinemura* is not whilst; in the Afon Hirnant in Wales (Hynes, 1961) *Amphinemura*, *Ephemerella* and *Baetis* are common, but *Gammarus* is absent.

Factors Influencing the Fauna

It would appear probable that the low winter numbers apparent at the three stations above are due, at least partly, to the effect of spates, which occur most frequently at that season of the year. All three of the substrates which were studied are unstable (this is particularly true of that at station A), and the scouring effect of the river during high water can reduce the density of the invertebrate fauna very considerably. During the summer months, the current at all three places is normally slower, and some silt and detritus settles out. Filamentous and other algae develop over the substrate and these in turn trap more silt. Under these favourable conditions the fauna builds up rapidly, partly by the asexual reproduction of certain species (e.g. *Stylaria lacustris* and *Nais pseudobtusa*) and also by the hatching of the eggs of certain summer forms (e.g. *Ephemerella ignita*) and of species which are multivoltine (e.g. *Baetis rhodani*). There is probably also some recruitment from fauna which may have escaped the rigorous winter conditions by burrowing deeply into the gravel (Badcock, 1949) or selecting some other favourable microhabitat (e.g. a weed bed).

Spates occurring subsequent to the development of this rich summer fauna may affect it drastically. The unstable nature of the substrates under conditions of high spate causes the coating of algae and silt to be sloughed off, and much of the invertebrate fauna is apparently lost with it. Many animals may be lost at this time (Allen, 1951; Logan, 1963), but as just mentioned some of them may escape by selecting temporarily a more stable microhabitat. Fauna which is carried along passively by the river has been termed "organic drift", and this has been studied in detail by several workers (e.g. Needham, 1928; Ide, 1942; Dendy, 1944; Müller, 1954; and Horton, 1961). These workers have shown that in the rivers which they studied there was a continuous flow of small invertebrates downstream, and that these formed an important source of food for various fish. Sampling in the River Endrick has indicated that the amount of drift fauna in most places here is of a low order, except below lake outfalls and during spates.

Dendy (1944) found that almost all species occurring in the bottom fauna can be found in the drift at some time, and the results of Müller (1954) are essentially the same. Moffett (1936), Müller (1954) and Hynes (1960) have shown that newly flooded water courses are rapidly colonized by many species of invertebrates—most of these presumably having drifted down from areas further upstream. Hynes (1960) notes that the animals which colonize such areas most rapidly are those which are mobile and fairly readily swept away by the current. Species with good hold-fast mechanisms are much slower in distributing themselves in this manner. In many aquatic invertebrates a positive rheotaxy helps to overcome the effect of being drifted downstream; and in certain adult insects (e.g. Trichoptera) it has been shown that the females fly upstream before ovipositing (Roos, 1957).

There appears to be no definition in the literature as to the minimum flow in a river which may be regarded as constituting a spate. Mills (1964) classes a flow of six times the normal average as severe; in the present account an arbitrary figure of eight times the average flow has been selected as being a severe spate, and in Fig. 10 the occurrence of high spates of this size (and greater) at Randieford on the River Endrick during 1960 is shown against the density of the bottom fauna at station A, the most unstable of the substrates studied. It can be seen that the high density of the summer months coincided with the absence of such spates, and that during their period of occurrence the density of the bottom fauna at station A was low. It should be noted here that whilst there is no doubt that the effect of spates on the density of the bottom fauna is an important one, there are also several other contributory factors. Thus the increased temperature and daylength during the summer months (Fig. 8) mean that conditions are much more favourable for the development of most algae (and subsequently of the bottom fauna) at this time of year than at other times. A rapid increase in the density of the bottom fauna therefore (especially asexually reproducing forms) is much more likely in any given stable period during summer than at other times of the year.

Several other workers have demonstrated the reducing effect of spates on the density of bottom fauna in rivers (e.g. Badcock, 1949; Allen, 1951; and Harrison and Elsworth, 1958). The winter minimum of invertebrate fauna found in some parts of the River Endrick has also been noted in other rivers (Badcock, 1953a), but in several rivers a maximum density has been recorded at this time (Hynes, 1960). It is suggested that such maxima are due to the presence of numerous small nymphs which have hatched from eggs laid there during the previous autumn; it would seem that the stability of the substrate and the frequency of spates are critical factors in this connection, and clearly these will vary both in space and in time.

Spates may not only affect the bottom fauna quantitatively but

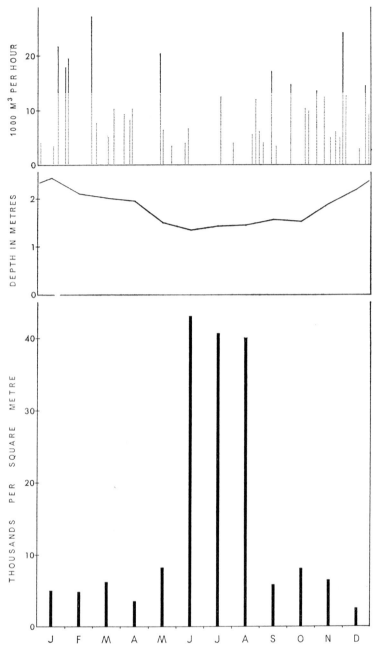

Fig. 10.—The peak flows at Randieford, water depths at Woodend and densities of invertebrate fauna at Woodend during 1960

98

also alter its character qualitatively. Thus at station A the only animals which are able to maintain themselves during the unstable winter conditions are burrowing species such as *Limnodrilus longus*, *Stictochironomus pictulus* and *Pisidium henslowanum*. These are augmented during the summer by surface dwelling species, e.g. *Hydra vulgaris*, *Chaetogaster diaphanus*, etc. At stations B and C the effect of spates appears to be less drastic, the substrate being more stable, and the normal current faster than at station A. Thus crawling forms (e.g. *Baetis rhodani*), clinging forms (e.g. *Simulium equinum*) and burrowing forms (e.g. *Lumbriculus variegatus*) are common here at all times of the year.

Few invertebrate species occurred commonly at both station A and station B. *Hydra vulgaris* is one of the few exceptions and was common during the summer at both places; its abundance at these stations illustrates the difference between the stability of the substrate at these two places. At both stations the species first appeared in numbers in June, and at both it was common for the next two months. A spate which occurred in September, however, (Fig. 10) affected both populations considerably, that at station A being extinguished, that at station B being reduced considerably in number, but a proportion of the population still remaining. A similar sequence of events took place with the populations of *Alona affinis* and *Stylaria lacustris*, both of which occurred at these two stations.

The total numbers of species recorded at stations A, B and C were 50, 85 and 88 respectively. Moon (1934) found that the community of a stony shore in Lake Windermere was much richer in the number of species than that of a sandy shore there; this certainly appears to be true also of the stony substrates at Drumtian and in the Altquhur Burn when compared to the sandy substrate at Woodend. As Moon (1934) has pointed out, this difference is probably due to the greater number of microhabitats offered by the former type of substrate. The difference is especially notable in the winter communities of these substrates, for, as pointed out above, all the species found at station A at this time are burrowing forms, whilst at stations B and C burrowing, crawling and clinging types are equally common.

Elton (1946) noted that in most habitats the number of genera represented was relatively high, but that the number of species there was low. In a survey of many different habitats occurring in Great Britain he showed that 86 per cent of the genera present were represented by only one species, the average number of species per genus being 1·38. This appears to be true also of the three communities studied here: at station A 89 per cent of the genera were represented by only one species and there was an average of 1·08 species per genus; at station B too 89 per cent of the genera had only one species, the number of species per genus here being 1·37; at station C 94 per cent of the genera had only one species and there was an average of 1·21 species per genus. Elton (1946) has noted that such figures differ greatly from those of a particular region (as distinct from a habitat); thus the average number of species per genus in all British insects is 4·23. This difference is attributed to historical or existing effects of competition between closely related species.

It has been pointed out elsewhere (Maitland, 1964a) that one of the most valuable features of quantitative data is their comparative value, and also that when comparing the results of different studies gravimetric data are preferable to numerical ones—especially where different mesh sizes have been used to obtain the samples, and where general aspects of biomass and productivity are being considered. The average standing crop found to be present at station A during 1960 was about 8 g./m² and that at station B about 16 g./m². It is not possible to give accurate comparable figures for station C where collections were made in a different year and were taken on a time rather than an area basis. However, it has been estimated that the area collected over in 10 minutes by the method used here was approximately 1 m², and so the average weight of bottom fauna during 1961 was of the order of 9 g./m². All these figures indicate that the standing crops of these substrates in the River Endrick are of intermediate richness when compared with the few available for rivers elsewhere in the world (e.g. Needham, 1934; Surber, 1936; Idyll, 1943; Allen, 1951; and Berg, 1948) where values of 5 to 20 g./m² have been found on sandy substrates, and 4 to 166 g./m² on stony substrates.

Plate Vᴀ.—The lower reaches of the River Endrick at station 2 (Woodend) looking downstream in winter. The current here is slow and the river broad and deep with many meanders. The sandy substrate in mid-stream here was one of the habitats (station A) chosen for regular qualitative sampling (cf. Plate Iᴀ)

Plate Vʙ.—The Loup of Fintry, where the River Endrick drops through a height of about 30 m., the waterfalls so formed acting as a complete barrier to Salmon and Sea Trout migrating upstream. Station 9 (Fintry) is a short distance below this point (Plate IIʙ)

Plate VIA.—A typical stretch of the Altquhur Burn, an important tributary of the River Endrick where many of the Salmon, Trout, Minnows and Stone Loach examined during the present study were collected. This is also the area where *Bathynella natans* (Plate IVB) occurs, living interstitially among beds of coarse gravel such as the one shown here (Maitland, 1962a)

Plate VIB.—The right bank of the River Endrick at Balfron, a short distance below the discharge of the sewage effluent from Balfron village (June, 1961). The cloudy water passing downstream from this effluent can be seen here close to the river's edge. The solid matter in this effluent settles out and causes silting of the stony substrate with subsequent drastic effects on the invertebrate fauna

V. The Vertebrate Fauna

Fish

Hunter, Slack and Hunter (1959) have recently published an account of the fish occurring in the Loch Lomond area. This is the most authentic species list for the area which has been published so far, and it brings up to date the older records of Brown (1891), Lumsden and Brown (1895), Scott and Brown (1901) and Lamond (1931). Of the nineteen species verified for the area in recent years by Hunter, Slack and Hunter (1959) four occur only in brackish water. The fifteen other species are all found in Loch Lomond itself, and, of these, fourteen have recently been recorded in the River Endrick. In addition to these, two further species have been collected in recent years in the Endrick valley, one catalogued by Hunter, Slack and Hunter (1959), but not authenticated by them, and the other mentioned only briefly by Lamond (1931) but not by any of the other authors mentioned above. The only species recorded from Loch Lomond, but not so far from the River Endrick, is the Ten-spined Stickleback—*Pygosteus pungitius* (L.).

The distribution of fish species in the River Endrick is given in Fig. 11. The species present in different parts of the river were collected in various ways, according to the nature of the water in that stretch. Direct observation during fine weather often gave a good idea of most of the common species present; species taken accidentally during invertebrate fauna collecting were noted also. In the smaller, shallower parts of the river most fish were caught either by means of a handnet or an electric fish-shocker. In the lower stretches of the river, where the water is deep, seine nets and fish traps were the commonest methods of capture adopted.

Cyclostomata—Petromyzontia

Petromyzon marinus (L.). The Sea Lamprey has been recorded from the River Endrick by MacDonald (1959), Hunter, Slack and

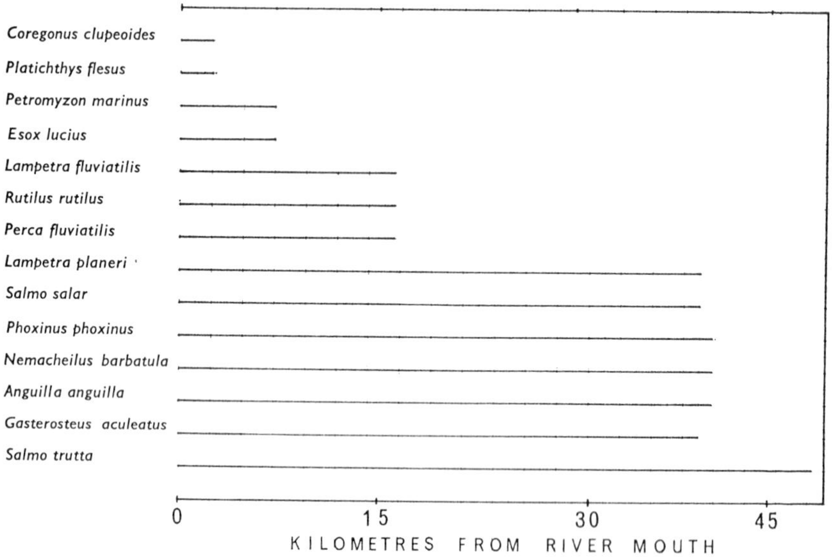

Fig 11.—The distribution of fish species in the River Endrick

Hunter (1959) and the present author. Though Hunter, Slack and Hunter (1959) suggest that this species breeds in the upper parts of the River Endrick, it seems unlikely that it could surmount the fall at the Pot of Gartness, and it is probably restricted to the lower reaches of the river. Certainly it is from there that all the specimens found in recent years have been recorded—including the 49 ammocoete larvae examined by MacDonald (1959).

Lampetra fluviatilis (L.). The River Lamprey is commoner than the Sea Lamprey in the River Endrick, and like it is probably restricted to the lower reaches. MacDonald (1959) examined 288 ammocoete larvae of this species from this part of the river, and during the present study adults have been found spawning under large boulders at station 3 (Drymen).

Lampetra planeri (Bloch). The Brook Lamprey is abundant in many parts of the middle and lower reaches of the River Endrick, and also in most tributaries, especially where the substrate consists of fine gravel or sand with some organic detritus. It is certainly the most abundant of the three species of lamprey found in the river, and is the only one which is known to occur above the Pot of Gartness.

Actinopterygii—Teleostei

Salmo salar (L.). Salmon are found in all parts of the middle and lower reaches of the River Endrick and in most tributaries. The young fish are most abundant in the middle reaches and certain tributaries, where they form an important part of the fish community (see below), whilst the adults are caught regularly in most parts of the main river below the Loup of Fintry during their spawning migration in autumn (Fig. 20).

Salmo trutta (L.). Trout occur in all parts of the River Endrick and this is probably the most abundant fish species present. Like Salmon, the young fish are most common in the middle reaches and many tributaries where the numbers of Trout are normally far greater than those of any other species. Both Sea Trout (*Salmo trutta trutta* L.) and Brown Trout (*Salmo trutta fario* L.) are found: it is impossible to distinguish between the young of these two forms, and it is probable that both make up the population of young Trout present in the middle and lower reaches of the river—certainly both types of adult are found there. As noted above, however, the upper reaches are separated from the rest of the river by the Loup of Fintry (Plate VB), a waterfall which is over 30 m. in height, and it is extremely unlikely that Sea Trout (or Salmon) are ever able to surmount this obstacle. Above it, therefore, the population consists entirely of Brown Trout: few other fish species have ever been seen there. This species is found in all parts of the upper reaches, though near the source it appears to be rare, and only a few small individuals occur in the pools there. The growth of Trout in the upper reaches of the River Endrick is notably slower than that of those further downstream (Dr. T.A. Stuart, personal communication).

Salmo irideus (Gibbons). The Rainbow Trout has been recorded on only one occasion from Loch Lomond, by Lamond (1931), and the species is not listed by Hunter, Slack and Hunter (1959). None had been recorded from the River Endrick until 1964, when a single specimen of about 2 kg. was angled in the middle reaches. A short time later a second, somewhat smaller, specimen was taken, also by an angler. It appears probable that these specimens were stray fish from stock introduced by man somewhere in the Clyde area.

Coregonus clupeoides (Lacépède). Powan are abundant in Loch Lomond, but appear to occur in the River Endrick only occasionally. The only recent record of this species from the river is of a single large specimen collected in the extreme lower reaches of the river near the mouth by seine net (Dr. H. D. Slack, personal communication).

Phoxinus phoxinus (L.). Minnows are common in most parts of the river, except the upper reaches, and they form an important part of the community of small fish found in the middle reaches and most tributaries which is discussed below. A detailed study of the spawning cycle of this species has been carried out in the Endrick valley by Scott (1963) on the population present in Loch Walton, a small reservoir just north of the Loup of Fintry (Fig. 2). It was shown that the main spawning period here is during May, June and July, and this agrees with the author's own observations carried out elsewhere in the Endrick valley during the same period.

Rutilus rutilus (L.). Roach are abundant in the lower reaches of the River Endrick, especially in the slow-flowing stretches below Drymen. The bulk of the population appears to spawn, however, in the faster-flowing water above this, and each year there is an impressive upstream migration to the spawning areas. These consist for the most part of large beds of *Myriophyllum* amd *Potamogeton* on which the sticky eggs are laid, though numbers of eggs are also found on gravel in the surrounding areas. This upstream migration of Roach for spawning purposes is evidently not an uncommon habit (Day, 1880), and the normal population of the River Endrick is probably augmented at spawning time by an influx of fish from Loch Lomond. In the River Endrick the fish migrate upstream each year just before the spawning period (June), often in very large numbers. The present observations confirm those of Ure (1795), who pointed out that the migration takes place within the space of a few days and that during this time the vast shoals of Braise (Roach) which come up the River Endrick from Loch Lomond were at one time caught by nets in thousands. After the eggs hatch, most of the fry appear to pass downstream (cf. Minnow, below), for though uncommon in the spawning areas they can be seen in large shoals in the slow-flowing reaches below.

Nemacheilus barbatula (L.). Loach are common in most parts of the River Endrick except the upper reaches above the Loup of Fintry. They make up an important part of the community of small fish discussed below, common in the middle reaches of the river and most tributaries. This species is most abundant on sandy and stony substrates where there is a moderate current, and especially where there is some weed cover.

Anguilla anguilla (L.). Eels are common in most parts of the River Endrick, especially in the middle reaches. None have been found in the upper reaches above the Loup of Fintry, but it is possible that some may occur there, for the species is common in Loch Walton, the main tributary stream of which flows higher than the top of this waterfall.

Esox lucius (L.). Pike have been recorded only from the extreme lower reaches of the River Endrick, where they are common, especially among weed beds. They are known to spawn here, for fry of the current year have occasionally been collected with samples of invertebrate fauna from among weed. The few specimens from the River Endrick whose stomachs were examined were found to have been feeding on small Roach.

Gasterosteus aculeatus (L.). Three-spined Sticklebacks are found only in the lower reaches, parts of the middle reaches and certain tributaries in the Endrick system. They spawn commonly among weed beds in still water in these stretches, and fry are abundant there during the summer months.

Perca fluviatilis (L.). Perch are common throughout the lower reaches of the River Endrick, and spawn regularly in many of the slow-flowing stretches of the river below Drymen. Several specimens recently collected from these reaches were found to have been feeding on ammocoete larvae there (Dr. H. D. Slack, personal communication).

Platichthys flesus (L.). Flounders, though not uncommon in Loch Lomond, have been recorded from the River Endrick on only a few occasions—always in the lower reaches.

As mentioned above, the Ten-spined Stickleback—*Pygosteus pungitius*—is not uncommon in Loch Lomond but has not so far been found in the River Endrick. It is possible, however, that this species could occur there. The only other species of fish found in the Endrick valley, but not so far recorded from the River Endrick itself or Loch Lomond, is the Common Carp—*Cyprinus carpio* (L.). This species was listed by Scott and Brown (1901) as occurring in various ponds in the Clyde area, though Hunter, Slack and Hunter (1959) note that there are no recent records from the Loch Lomond District. In 1959, however, a small artificial loch in the middle reaches of the Endrick valley was found to contain a well-established population of this species (Maitland, 1964*b*), and it is not unlikely that specimens may occasionally make their way downstream into the lower reaches of the River Endrick and Loch Lomond. Tench—*Tinca tinca* (L.)—are recorded by Brown (1891) and by Lumsden and Brown (1895) from the mouth of the River Endrick, but have not been recorded in recent years by Hunter, Slack and Hunter (1959), and none was seen during the present survey.

Amphibia, Birds and Mammals

Other vertebrates are for the most part less intimately associated with water than fish; nevertheless many species of amphibia, birds and mammals are aquatic by nature and may profoundly affect the ecology of the freshwater community with which they are associated. On this account it was felt justifiable to include here a short statement of those aquatic vertebrates which are common in the valley of the River Endrick, thus making this ecological account a more complete one.

Amphibia are found only rarely in the main river, but in the many slow-flowing ditches and small ponds (including ox-bow lakes) occurring near the lower reaches of the River Endrick five species of this class are common, and are known to breed at the appropriate times of the year. These species are: the Great Crested Newt, *Triturus cristatus cristatus* (Laurenti); Smooth Newt, *Triturus vulgaris vulgaris* (L.); Palmate Newt, *Triturus helveticus* (Razoumoski); Common Frog, *Rana temporaria temporaria* (L.); and Common Toad, *Bufo bufo bufo* (L.). Only the Palmate Newt and the Common Frog are found in the upper parts of the Endrick Valley, where both are common in bog pools and ditches.

Many species of aquatic birds are found on the River Endrick, the most important species probably being Dipper, *Cinclus cinclus* (L.); Heron, *Ardea cinerea* (L.); Red-breasted Merganser, *Mergus serrator* (L.); and Moorhen, *Gallinula chloropus* (L.). Other species which have been recorded include Kingfisher, *Alcedo ispida* (L.); Osprey, *Pandion haliaetus* (L.); Cormorant, *Phalacrocorax carbo* (L.); Whooper Swan, *Cygnus cygnus* (L.); Mute Swan, *Cygnus olor* (Gmelin); Sheld Duck, *Tadorna tadorna* (L.); Mallard, *Anas boschas* (L.); Shoveler, *Spatula clypeata* (L.); Teal, *Querquedula crecca* (L.); Wigeon, *Mareca penelope* (L.); Pochard, *Nyroca ferina* (L.); Tufted Duck, *Nyroca fuligula* (L.); Scaup, *Aythya marila* (L.); Golden-eye, *Clangula glaucion* (L.); Goosander, *Mergus merganser* (L.); Water Rail, *Rallus aquaticus* (L.); Coot, *Fulica atra* (L.); Oyster Catcher, *Haematopus ostralegus* (L.); Common Snipe, *Gallinago gallinago* (L.); Common Sandpiper, *Totanus hypoleucus* (L.); Redshank, *Totanus totanus* (L.); Common Tern, *Sterna hirudo* (L.); Arctic Tern, *Sterna paradisea* (Brunnick); Blackheaded Gull, *Larus ridibundus* (L.); Common Gull, *Larus canus* (L.); and Herring Gull, *Larus argentatus* (Gmelin).

Dippers are common in the middle and upper reaches of the River Endrick and many pairs nest there each year. Herons occur in all parts of the river valley, but are particularly common in the lower reaches, where there is a well-established heronry not far from the main river. All the fish observed to have been caught by Herons in the lower reaches were Roach, but presumably different species are taken in other parts of the river. Red-breasted Mergansers are most common on the lower and middle reaches of the river, where they appear to feed mainly on small salmonids, as Mills (1962) found in several rivers in the north of Scotland. Moorhens are most common in the lower reaches of the river, and nests are common there during summer among emergent vegetation at the edge. The stomach of a female of this species found dead in the Altquhur Burn in 1961 was found to contain filamentous algae and several Hydracarina.

Few aquatic mammals are of importance in the valley of the River Endrick. The Water Shrew, *Neomys fodiens bicolor* (Shaw), has been recorded in Stirlingshire by Millais (1906) and Sword (1908), but there are no recent records of this species in the area. They are known by the author to be common elsewhere in the Clyde area less than

8

5 km. from the Endrick watershed, and it would seem probable that they occur in the Endrick valley also. The Water Vole, *Arvicola amphibius* (L.), is common along the edge of the River Endrick in the lower reaches, where it feeds on aquatic vegetation. The Otter, *Lutra lutra* (L.), has been recorded in the area on many occasions, and tracks are not uncommon along parts of the river bank. It is probable that several pairs are resident in the Endrick valley; their impact on fish stocks is uncertain, though they are known to feed on adult Salmon and Trout in the river.

VI. A Study of a Fish Community

As noted above there are five species of fish which are common in the middle reaches and most tributaries of the River Endrick— Salmon (*Salmo salar*), Trout (*Salmo trutta*), Minnow (*Phoxinus phoxinus*), Stone Loach (*Nemacheilus barbatula*) and Three-spined Stickleback (*Gasterosteus aculeatus*). This area is the one therefore which is important for the production of game fish, and because of this an attempt was made to study this community in some detail, particularly with regard to the feeding relationships between the above five species and also between these fish and the bottom fauna present in the same area. Most of the detailed data regarding these feeding relationships have been published elsewhere (Maitland, 1965) whilst details of the quantitative aspects of the invertebrate fauna of the main area studied (the Altquhur Burn) have already been given above. The present account is an attempt to synthesize these and other aspects of the ecology of this community.

Relatively few workers have examined the feeding relationships within a community of fish (Swynnerton and Worthington, 1940; Frost, 1946; Hartley, 1948; etc.), most past studies being concerned with a single species. Thus all five species which were studied here have been the subject of analyses at one time or another, though never all together. The food of Salmon has been examined by Pentelow, Southgate and Bassindale (1933), Moon (1936), Frost and Went (1940), Carpenter (1940) and Allen (1941); the food of Trout by Pentelow (1932), Slack (1934), Allen (1938), Neill (1938), Frost (1939), Horton (1961), McCormack (1962) and others; the food of Minnows by Frost (1943), of Stone Loach by Smyly (1955), and of Three-spined Sticklebacks by Hynes (1950). The food relationships of two or more of these species (but never all five) have been analysed by Soong (1938), Frost (1950), Thomas (1962) and Mills (1964) (Salmon and Trout); Frost (1943) and Badcock (1949) (Trout and Minnows); Smyly (1955) (Trout, Minnows and Stone Loach); and

Hartley (1948) (Trout, Minnows, Stone Loach and Three-spined Sticklebacks).

A few of the above studies of single species have been concerned not only with the food eaten by the fish, but also with the food available to the fish from the bottom fauna (e.g. Neill, 1938; Allen, 1941; and Horton, 1961). There appear to be very few studies available, however, which examine the feeding relationships of all the species of fish and the bottom fauna present in the same habitat, and this was one of the primary purposes of the present study (Maitland, 1965).

Methods

Whilst the five species of fish concerned in this account are found in greatest numbers in the middle reaches of the main river, this part of the River Endrick was not chosen for detailed study for two reasons. Firstly, the river here offers several habitats, which might tend to complicate any assessment of competition, and secondly, the large size of the river in the middle reaches makes the capture of fish difficult at normal water levels and almost impossible during spates. It was decided, therefore, that it would be preferable to study the ecology of this community in one or more of the tributary streams flowing into the main river, and after an initial survey in August, 1960, of several of the most likely of these, the Altquhur Burn was chosen for regular sampling.

The Altquhur Burn is some 10 km. long and enters the lower reaches of the River Endrick on the right bank some distance below the Pot of Gartness (Fig. 2). It rises in moorland at a height of 335 m., and after about 1 km. its waters have been dammed to form Muirpark Reservoir, a small body of water which supports a resident population of Brown Trout. For much of the rest of its course the Altquhur Burn is like many of those found in the Endrick valley, with a rocky bed and small pools which alternate with stretches of riffle. In its lower reaches, however, the stream has cut through a series of sand, gravel and clay beds, and the substrate becomes much less stony, consisting for the most part of sand and coarse gravel (Maitland, 1962a). This stretch of the stream—which has a length of about 2 km.—was the one chosen for regular sampling; the conditions prevailing here have already been described above in the section dealing with quantitative studies.

During 1961, monthly samples of the bottom fauna of this stretch of the Altquhur Burn were taken, as described above (see Fig. 5c). In conjunction with these collections, samples of the fish present were also taken, these being caught by handnet. All fish were measured for length in the field and then returned to the stream, except those retained for stomach analysis, which were killed immediately using a concentrated anaesthetic.

Although Salmon, Trout, Minnows and Stone Loach are relatively common in the Altquhur Burn, Three-spined Sticklebacks are not, and consequently during the summer of 1961 four samples which included all five species were taken elsewhere in the Endrick system: two from the Balgair Burn, one from the Mar Burn and one from the main river at Drumtian (Fig. 2). All fish taken for stomach analysis were measured in the laboratory for length, then weighed, and their stomach contents were examined. Minnows, Stone Loach and Three-spined Sticklebacks were not aged, but scales were removed from the larger specimens of Salmon and Trout for this purpose.

Several methods have been employed in the past by various workers to enumerate the stomach contents of fish, and these have been critically reviewed by Hynes (1950). He points out that these methods are of three main types: numerical, occurrence and mass, the value of each depending on what exactly the investigator is attempting to analyze. The first two have the advantage of being relatively exact methods, but have the great disadvantage of not evaluating the differences in bulk between various food items. Thus a single large food organism may be many times the size of several small ones, though numerically it would count as much less. Accurate estimates of the mass of different food items are usually difficult to obtain, largely due to the small size of the organisms concerned and the fact that they may be partly digested or coated with sticky mucus. Methods of estimating the mass of such food items have varied from the very crude method of Swynnerton and Worthington (1940) to the more exact points methods adopted by Hynes (1950) and Smyly

(1955). The principal disadvantage of such points methods is that they tend to be subjective, and the value of each food item is related more to the size of the stomach than to its own mass.

In the present study all three methods were used in the recording of stomach contents. The bulk of different food items was estimated by a method similar to that used by Horton (1961), but which was evolved independently by the author. Each food item was measured to the nearest millimetre and was afterwards given a number of points according to its estimated bulk. This method is partly after that of Ricker (1937), who based his values on the smallest food organism found, to which he gave one point (equal to approximately 0·01 mg.). Here too, a minimum value of one point was given to those animals with an estimated weight of 0·01 mg., though only a few of the smaller Chironomidae and Copepoda were as small as this. Most of the food organisms were much larger, and it was often possible to check estimated weights of these by the direct weighing of whole specimens.

Numerical methods alone have been used extensively by Allen (1941 and 1951) who is very critical of points systems of the type advocated by Hynes (1950). It is freely admitted that the present method is open to criticism on several counts, and that at best the results obtained for each food organism are only an approximation to its true bulk. The system, however, is at least a practicable one which is in some ways more versatile than the points methods of Hynes (1950) and Smyly (1955); and it would certainly seem to offer a more satisfactory assessment than does the numerical method of Allen (1941).

The percentage composition of the food of each species or group of fish was calculated for each collection, and the results of different collections then summed for any required comparison. For such comparisons only collections which include all the species under consideration are used, hence the reason for keeping the primary data in Tables 8 and 9 separate.

The Fish Community

Though the method of sampling the fish was no doubt to some extent selective, some general observations can be made about the populations present in the Altquhur Burn and elsewhere in the River Endrick. Trout is by far the commonest species, as noted above, and in many places is more numerous than all the others together. Salmon are much less common: the ratio between the two species apparently being related to the number of adults which spawned in the river in previous years (see below). Minnows and Stone Loach are also less abundant than Trout, but are present at most places in the middle reaches and in most tributaries. Three-spined Sticklebacks, on the other hand, are more erratic in their distribution, and are mostly found in slow-moving water where weed-cover is available. Where they do occur, however, they are usually common. In the Altquhur Burn, only a few specimens were found during the present study.

Eels also were taken occasionally here, and Brook Lampreys were abundant in some places—though this species was not normally caught by the fishing method used here. Other important vertebrates noted in the Altquhur Burn from time to time were Herons (*Ardea cinerea*), Dippers (*Cinclus cinclus*), Moorhens (*Gallinula chloropus*), Red-breasted Mergansers (*Mergus serrator*) and Otters (*Lutra lutra*), all of which, no doubt, may have some significant effects on the community discussed here.

This community in the River Endrick is essentially one of small fish, as can be seen from Fig. 12. The lengths of each species overlap considerably with those of all the others, almost all specimens being from 1 to 15 cm. in length. Greatest overlapping occurs in the 2 to 10 cm. range, and this size similarity is probably an important factor in connection with competition between these fish (Maitland, 1965).

All five species are known to spawn in many of the tributary streams examined, and many of the data in Fig. 13 agree with this: the 1st year fish usually being present in some numbers except in the case of the Minnow, where 1st year fish are often rare in the tributary streams—this in spite of the fact that many adults may have spawned there earlier in the year. The only exception to this in the

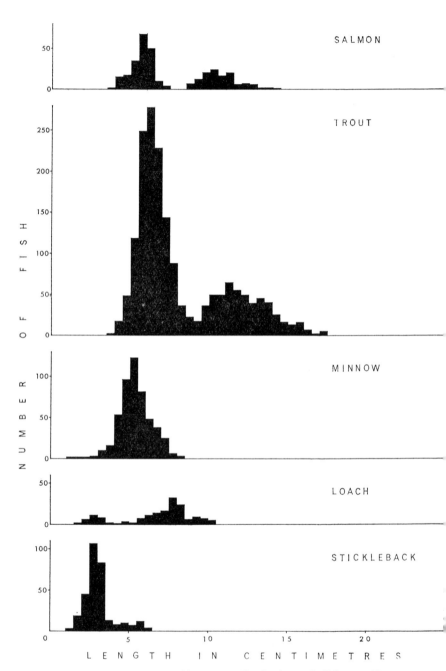

Fig. 12.—The length/frequency distribution of Salmon, Trout, Minnows, Stone Loach and Three-spined Sticklebacks in the Endrick system during August 1960 and 1961

114

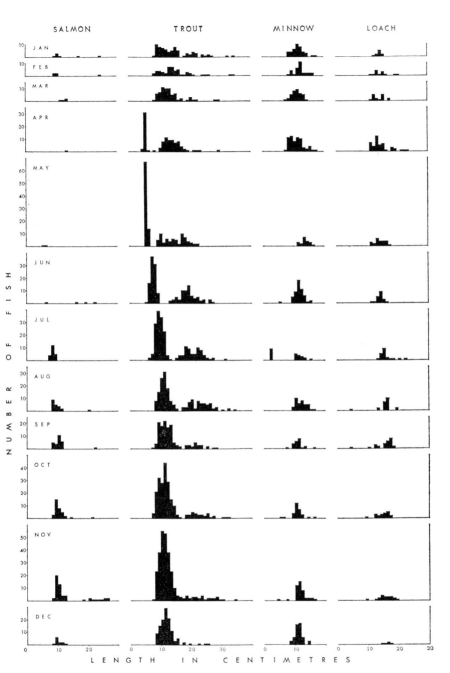

Fig. 13.—The monthly length/frequency distribution of Salmon, Trout, Minnows and Stone Loach in the Altquhur Burn during 1961

115

streams examined in the Endrick system was in the Burn of Mar in 1961, where fry were common in some stretches. A careful search in many of the streams from which fry were not recorded during routine sampling revealed at most an occasional few at the edges of the larger pools. It would appear that, after hatching in the tributaries, the majority of the fry of this species must pass downstream, either actively or carried by the current into the main river, where 1st year fish are always abundant and occur in large shoals, often consisting of many thousands of fish. The same situation may be true to a lesser extent of Stone Loach fry, which are certainly much more abundant in the main river than in any of the tributary burns. The situation is a comparable one to that observed among Roach in the lower reaches of the River Endrick, and discussed above.

The monthly length/frequencies of Salmon, Trout, Minnows and Stone Loach in the Altquhur Burn during 1961 are given in Fig. 13. Salmon are not abundant here, especially during the winter months; though it is known from sampling elsewhere in the River Endrick that the fry emerge from the gravel in April (at the same time as Trout), very few were seen here until July. It has been suggested (Dr. T. A. Stuart, personal communication) that the adult Salmon spawn only in the lower part of this stream and in the main river, and that the fry gradually migrate upstream after hatching. After July, the fry are common in the Altquhur Burn. Some of the larger male parr collected here in October and November were ripe, and presumably spawn with adult females at this time, as is known to happen in other rivers (Jones and King, 1952). Trout are abundant here at all times, the fry emerging in April and growing rapidly during the summer months as discussed below. Minnows and Stone Loach were normally common but never abundant in the Altquhur Burn.

Feeding Habits

The feeding relationships of Salmon, Trout, Minnows, Stone Loach and Three-spined Sticklebacks in the River Endrick have been discussed in full elsewhere (Maitland, 1965) and here only certain aspects relevant to the present community analysis are considered. A comparison of the food of Salmon, Trout, Minnows and Stone

Loach in the Altquhur Burn during 1961 is given in Table 8, and in Table 9 the food of these four species and of Three-spined Stickle-backs elsewhere in the Endrick system during the summer of 1961 is catalogued.

It can be seen that many of the aquatic food organisms listed were eaten by all five species and that some were obviously of major importance to them all (e.g. *Gammarus*, *Baetis* and *Orthocladius*). However, although the diets of these fish were in some ways similar qualitatively, there were characteristic quantitative differences. Thus one of the major items in the diet of young Salmon was undoubtedly the quantity of Ephemeroptera and Plecoptera nymphs eaten: whilst in contrast to this, young Trout ate fewer of these but instead fed on large numbers of surface organisms. The major item in the diet of Minnows was undoubtedly algae (see Maitland, 1965), whilst Stone Loach fed particularly on various species of larval Chironomidae. To Three-spined Sticklebacks, too, larval Chironomidae were of importance, and this was the only species other than Minnow to eat algae.

As noted elsewhere, some 89 different species of invertebrate have been recorded from that part of the Altquhur Burn which was investigated for this study; it is of some interest to note here the extent to which the variety of food eaten there by the fish species reflects the nature of this invertebrate fauna. All four species of fish which were common in this burn ate a wide variety of the inverte-brates commonly found in the substrate there, and an examination of a reasonable number of fish stomachs throughout the year should certainly indicate all the common members of the bottom fauna. Thus of the 89 species recorded during 1961 in bottom fauna samples, 45 were found in the stomachs of Salmon, 56 in Trout, 48 in Minnows and 50 in Stone Loach. The only aquatic invertebrate recorded from fish stomachs but not from bottom fauna collections was *Bosmina coregoni*. This planktonic species is not normally found in streams, and it is probable that the specimens eaten by the fish were ones carried down from Muirpark Reservoir (where the species is common) as part of the "organic drift" described by Müller (1954).

A comparison of the general composition of the bottom fauna of the Altquhur Burn during 1961 with that of the aquatic invertebrate

Table 8.—The percentage composition by Bulk (% B), by Occurrence (% O) and by Number (% N) of the food of Salmon, Trout, Minnows and Stone Loach in the Altquhur Burn during 1961

Food Organism	Salmon % B	% O	% N	Trout % B	% O	% N	Minnow % B	% O	% N	Loach % B	% O	% N
Lumbriculus	2·0	1·7	0·1	1·1	2·5	0·3	5·1	6·3	2·4	3·0	8·3	0·5
Eiseniella	0·6	3·7	0·1	1·4	3·3	0·3	4·6	3·1	1·2	—	—	—
Cyclops	—	—	—	—	—	—	0·1	0·4	0·1	0·1	0·4	0·1
Canthocamptus	0·1	0·4	0·1	—	—	—	—	—	—	—	—	—
Gammarus	2·4	6·4	0·6	16·3	35·4	6·1	8·1	13·9	3·9	6·4	61·6	2·6
Ephemerella	7·2	17·6	1·8	1·0	10·5	0·4	1·1	3·1	0·3	1·2	9·2	0·4
Ecdyonurus	1·6	8·1	0·3	0·2	2·3	0·1	0·4	1·0	0·2	0·6	2·6	0·1
Rhithrogena	0·1	2·1	0·1	—	—	—	—	—	—	—	—	—
Habrophlebia	0·2	0·8	0·1	1·1	7·9	0·4	—	—	—	0·7	3·5	3·4
Leptophlebia	0·6	3·3	—	1·1	3·5	0·3	0·9	1·5	0·4	4·9	10·8	1·8
Centroptilum	—	—	—	0·1	1·9	0·2	0·1	0·4	0·1	0·3	2·1	0·3
Baetis	36·4	67·9	25·2	5·5	23·9	3·5	9·6	20·6	6·2	17·8	35·6	11·6
Brachyptera	2·4	10·6	2·6	0·1	0·8	0·1	—	—	—	0·1	0·8	0·4
Protonemura	—	—	—	0·1	1·5	0·2	0·1	0·2	0·1	—	—	—
Amphinemura	2·7	10·8	4·7	0·9	10·2	1·7	0·5	2·5	1·3	5·1	25·4	5·0
Nemoura	1·3	8·9	2·0	2·8	14·8	2·9	3·3	7·9	3·1	3·6	13·0	2·1
Leuctra	4·6	21·5	2·9	0·9	12·8	0·6	0·5	2·1	0·4	6·7	29·7	2·6
Capnia	4·7	10·8	1·9	0·5	1·5	0·5	0·3	0·4	0·2	6·6	8·1	2·3
Isoperla	3·0	7·6	1·4	0·2	0·8	0·1	1·1	0·4	0·2	0·5	1·5	0·2
Anabolia	1·5	12·5	3·4	3·9	25·4	6·8	5·1	10·3	4·7	1·1	5·0	0·3
Hydropsyche	3·3	7·9	0·4	4·7	10·8	1·1	2·0	2·9	0·6	1·5	4·5	0·6
Polycentropus	0·4	1·3	0·1	1·4	7·1	0·6	1·9	2·7	0·4	2·6	10·2	0·8
Rhyacophila	0·6	5·2	0·1	0·1	0·8	0·1	0·7	0·8	0·4	0·3	1·3	0·1
Simulium	4·6	36·6	10·5	3·0	16·8	6·5	2·6	9·5	4·7	3·0	32·1	8·1
Pentaneura	0·1	2·1	2·7	0·3	10·9	0·4	1·2	8·0	2·5	2·7	42·2	4·5
Procladius	0·3	2·8	0·2	4·8	10·4	3·3	4·5	2·6	1·4	6·2	20·4	3·1
Stictochironomus	0·1	4·2	0·1	0·5	6·2	0·8	1·9	8·1	1·9	2·0	16·3	4·0
Endochironomus	0·1	0·7	0·1	0·1	2·1	0·3	0·1	0·4	0·2	—	—	—

Tanytarsus	1·1	20·8	3·8	0·7	25·3	3·7	2·7	10·8	10·1	1·8	35·7	7·1
Prodiamesa	0·2	5·1	0·2	0·7	10·3	0·6	2·0	7·2	2·4	6·2	26·0	5·1
Orthocladius	6·5	62·8	26·3	2·4	42·2	13·7	4·9	39·5	23·5	5·3	58·8	20·1
Corynoneura	0·1	5·6	0·2	0·1	5·3	0·4	0·1	2·1	0·1	0·1	3·3	0·2
Eukiefferiella	0·2	11·5	1·6	0·1	1·9	0·3	0·2	1·6	0·9	0·3	9·8	1·9
Cardiocladius	0·3	4·4	0·1	0·1	0·4	0·1	—	—	—	0·2	4·2	0·1
Trichocladius	1·3	11·8	0·2	0·5	13·5	1·3	2·0	13·8	4·2	2·8	28·3	4·3
Tipula	0·1	0·8	0·1	1·4	4·2	0·3	0·7	0·2	0·1	—	—	—
Limnophora	1·0	0·8	0·1	0·3	5·4	0·3	0·7	4·7	1·6	0·7	14·6	1·0
Dicranota	—	10·6	1·1	1·3	14·5	1·2	3·7	11·3	2·5	2·7	25·0	2·3
Bezzia	0·3	—	—	0·5	1·3	0·3	0·3	2·8	0·4	1·4	15·9	1·1
Hydroporus	0·8	1·6	0·1	0·5	6·2	0·3	0·7	2·3	0·4	0·2	2·9	0·1
Helmis	0·2	4·1	1·2	0·1	3·1	0·2	0·1	0·8	0·1	0·1	0·4	0·1
Esolus	0·1	3·8	0·3	0·1	0·4	0·1	0·2	1·7	0·1	—	—	—
Limnius	—	1·2	0·1	—	4·2	0·4	0·9	0·4	0·1	—	—	—
Hygrobates	0·7	—	—	0·1	—	—	0·1	12·5	4·3	0·1	0·4	0·5
Ancylus	—	5·0	0·6	0·1	0·8	0·1	0·4	0·4	0·1	0·1	0·4	—
Lymnaea	—	—	—	0·1	0·4	0·1	0·3	1·0	0·3	—	—	—
Pisidium	4·1	—	—	2·7	0·4	1·5	0·9	1·0	0·8	—	—	0·5
Other aquatic	—	7·6	0·5	—	10·2	—	11·8	4·9	3·3	0·8	9·6	—
Algae	0·4	—	—	2·3	—	0·6	—	23·5	—	—	—	—
S. Oligochaeta	0·1	0·7	0·1	0·3	5·2	0·9	—	—	—	—	—	0·1
S. Isopoda	—	1·1	0·1	1·9	5·4	1·2	—	—	—	0·2	0·7	0·1
S. Plecoptera	0·5	—	—	3·8	11·2	7·4	1·2	4·5	1·3	—	—	—
S. Hemiptera	—	4·8	0·5	0·4	34·7	0·7	0·1	0·9	0·1	0·2	3·9	0·1
S. Hymenoptera	0·1	—	—	1·0	8·9	0·3	0·1	0·4	0·1	—	—	—
S. Trichoptera	0·1	1·0	0·1	1·6	4·2	0·5	1·3	0·4	0·1	—	—	—
S. Lepidoptera	0·6	1·5	0·1	12·6	7·9	18·2	5·7	6·7	3·7	0·1	0·4	—
S. Diptera	0·1	10·1	0·8	8·2	47·7	5·5	0·2	6·8	2·1	0·2	1·3	—
S. Coleoptera	0·2	2·8	0·1	0·5	32·7	0·9	2·0	0·8	0·2	0·3	0·8	—
S. Araneida	—	1·8	0·2	1·6	8·5	0·6	1·2	2·3	0·6	—	—	—
S. Diplopoda	—	—	—	1·7	7·1	0·8	—	0·9	0·1	—	—	—
S. Mollusca	—	—	—	0·1	2·2	0·1	—	—	—	0·1	0·4	0·1
Other surface	—	—	—	—	1·0	—	—	—	—	0·1	0·4	0·1
Number of Fish		140			342			255			204	

Table 9.—The percentage composition by Bulk (% B), by Occurrence (% O) and by Number (% N) of the food of Salmon, Trout, Minnows, Stone Loach and Three-spined Stickleback in the Endrick system during 1961

Food Organism	Salmon % B	% O	% N	Trout % B	% O	% N	Minnow % B	% O	% N	Loach % B	% O	% N	Stickleback % B	% O	% N
Lumbriculus	—	—	—	0·1	1·3	0·1	0·3	1·1	0·2	2·8	4·8	0·3	3·1	3·8	0·2
Eisemiella	—	—	—	—	—	—	0·6	1·1	0·2	—	—	—	—	—	—
Cyclops	—	—	—	—	—	—	—	—	—	0·1	1·3	0·1	0·1	5·0	0·1
Canthocamptus	—	—	—	—	—	—	—	—	—	0·4	12·7	0·6	0·4	8·8	1·2
Gammarus	8·7	8·3	1·1	7·5	20·6	2·3	5·9	8·3	2·5	15·8	45·4	5·0	7·9	22·5	2·2
Ephemerella	5·6	20·0	2·7	2·2	15·0	0·4	1·7	3·8	0·9	3·2	12·5	1·0	4·4	12·5	0·8
Ecdyonurus	5·4	19·2	2·0	14·5	25·3	1·6	3·9	6·1	0·8	1·2	5·0	0·3	14·1	10·0	1·8
Rhithrogena	—	—	—	—	—	—	—	—	—	—	—	—	0·4	2·5	0·1
Habrophlebia	—	—	—	0·1	1·3	0·1	—	—	—	0·1	1·3	0·2	0·5	2·5	0·1
Leptophlebia	—	—	—	—	—	—	—	—	—	—	—	—	—	—	—
Centroptilum	27·0	40·3	9·6	1·9	17·8	0·7	2·2	9·6	3·0	13·2	28·3	5·1	2·5	6·3	0·4
Baetis	—	—	—	—	—	—	—	—	—	—	—	—	—	—	—
Brachyptera	—	—	—	—	—	—	0·8	8·8	1·3	—	—	—	—	—	—
Protonemura	0·1	5·0	0·6	0·2	8·8	0·3	—	—	—	—	—	—	0·1	1·3	0·1
Amphinemura	—	—	—	0·5	6·3	0·4	—	—	—	—	—	—	0·2	1·3	0·2
Nemoura	—	—	—	—	—	—	—	—	—	—	—	—	1·2	18·8	3·4
Leuctra	11·2	5·7	5·9	9·5	22·5	5·0	3·3	10·0	1·7	12·3	33·9	3·3	6·6	20·0	1·0
Capnia	0·1	5·0	0·3	0·1	2·5	0·1	0·6	1·3	0·3	—	—	—	—	—	—
Isoperla	0·7	10·0	0·6	3·6	15·6	1·1	2·4	12·3	2·5	—	—	—	—	—	—
Anabolia	2·6	4·2	0·3	0·6	3·8	0·1	—	—	—	1·1	10·0	0·5	1·8	13·8	1·7
Hydropsyche	0·2	5·0	0·3	0·7	6·3	0·1	—	—	—	0·5	2·5	0·2	4·0	2·5	0·2
Polycentropus	—	—	—	0·6	3·8	0·7	—	—	—	1·2	3·8	6·5	1·3	1·3	0·1
Rhyacophila	—	—	—	0·1	6·6	0·5	—	—	—	—	—	—	—	—	—
Simulium	1·6	15·8	4·0	0·5	9·4	0·3	2·0	2·5	0·5	1·6	32·9	2·2	0·5	16·3	1·0
Pentaneura	0·5	8·3	0·4	0·5	6·2	—	0·1	4·7	1·0	3·9	22·7	4·9	7·6	27·5	2·5
Procladius	0·3	10·0	0·9	—	—	—	0·1	1·1	0·3	7·2	18·1	—	4·8	12·5	1·3
Stictochironomus	—	—	—	—	—	—	1·0	5·0	1·7	—	—	—	—	—	—
Endochironomus	—	—	—	—	—	—	—	—	—	3·0	9·8	0·9	5·9	10·0	4·2
Tanytarsus	0·4	11·7	1·2	0·1	4·1	0·4	0·1	1·1	0·1	1·2	25·0	2·5	3·5	40·0	11·0

	37			76			84			70			80		
Prodiamesa	14·2	42·1	0·3	—	3·8	—	0·3	1·3	0·3	3·1	15·0	4·7	0·6	7·5	2·0
Orthocladius	0·1	62·9	5·4	36·6	—	22·8	39·0	53·6	2·8	58·8	85·0	20·6	56·6	83·8	16·0
Corynoneura	—	5·4	—	—	—	—	—	—	—	0·1	3·5	0·1	0·3	5·0	0·1
Eukiefferiella	—	—	—	—	—	—	—	—	—	—	—	—	—	—	—
Cardiocladius	1·7	24·6	1·0	6·2	—	0·9	1·0	6·8	0·4	1·4	11·5	3·2	3·6	5·0	0·4
Trichocladius	0·1	1·3	0·1	2·5	—	0·1	—	—	—	0·7	7·9	0·6	0·3	6·3	1·2
Tipula	—	—	—	1·6	—	0·1	—	—	—	—	—	—	—	—	—
Limnophora	—	—	—	2·8	—	0·2	0·7	5·0	0·3	0·1	1·0	0·3	—	—	—
Dicranota	0·3	10·0	0·6	3·7	—	0·1	0·4	2·5	0·2	0·2	3·8	0·2	—	—	—
Bezzia	—	—	—	3·1	—	0·2	0·8	5·0	0·4	0·1	2·5	0·1	0·1	2·5	0·5
Hydroporus	—	—	—	12·5	4·5	0·9	0·7	4·9	0·1	0·1	3·5	0·1	0·8	3·8	0·7
Helmis	3·4	22·5	4·2	2·5	1·8	0·1	0·3	1·1	0·7	0·1	1·2	0·1	0·5	7·3	1·1
Esolus	—	—	—	16·9	0·1	1·3	5·3	15·0	0·3	1·0	1·2	0·1	0·1	2·5	0·2
Limnius	1·1	12·9	1·3	1·3	—	0·1	12·8	10·9	5·3	—	4·2	0·4	1·5	12·5	3·2
Hygrobates	0·1	4·2	0·4	3·8	—	0·2	0·5	3·6	12·8	—	—	—	0·4	10·0	0·2
Ancylus	4·6	13·8	3·8	2·5	—	0·1	1·4	2·5	0·5	—	—	—	0·5	6·3	1·9
Lymnaea	—	—	—	—	—	—	—	—	—	—	—	—	0·2	3·8	0·6
Pisidium	3·2	15·4	1·3	21·9	—	1·4	1·7	3·5	1·8	—	—	—	—	—	—
Other aquatic	—	15·4	—	—	—	—	0·4	55·7	55·1	0·2	2·3	0·6	0·7	10·0	0·4
Algae	—	—	—	2·5	—	0·1	—	2·5	1·8	—	—	—	—	2·5	0·2
S. Oligochaeta	0·9	4·2	0·3	2·5	0·5	0·3	0·5	2·3	0·9	—	—	—	—	—	—
S. Isopoda	0·6	10·4	3·0	40·6	1·9	7·9	1·9	4·8	0·3	—	—	—	—	—	—
S. Plecoptera	0·8	6·3	0·7	25·0	1·2	2·3	1·2	1·3	0·1	—	—	—	—	—	—
S. Hemiptera	—	—	—	—	—	—	—	—	—	—	—	—	—	—	—
S. Hymenoptera	—	—	—	5·0	—	0·2	—	—	—	—	—	—	—	—	—
S. Trichoptera	3·6	27·5	10·6	78·1	—	43·6	—	—	—	—	—	—	—	—	—
S. Lepidoptera	0·9	5·4	0·4	26·6	—	2·0	—	—	—	—	—	—	—	—	—
S. Diptera	—	—	—	5·0	30·5	0·3	12·0	23·6	3·2	0·1	2·3	0·1	0·1	1·3	0·1
S. Coleoptera	—	—	—	2·8	4·4	0·2	2·0	4·7	1·0	—	—	—	—	—	—
S. Araneida	—	—	—	—	0·4	—	0·1	1·1	0·2	—	—	—	—	—	—
S. Diplopoda	—	—	—	—	0·9	—	—	—	—	—	—	—	—	—	—
S. Mollusca	—	—	—	—	—	—	—	—	—	—	—	—	—	—	—
Other surface	—	—	—	5·0	0·5	0·3	—	—	—	—	—	—	—	—	—
Number of Fish		37			76			84			70			80	

food eaten there by Salmon, Trout, Minnows and Stone Loach is given in Fig. 14. The general similarity between them is close, the most important members of the bottom fauna being those most eaten by the fish. It should be noted that the results for the diet of each species of fish are treated entirely on the basis of the amount of aquatic invertebrate food eaten and are not comparable to those discussed elsewhere which include surface organisms as well as algae and other aquatic food such as fish and fish ova.

The availability of bottom fauna to various fish species has been discussed by Neill (1938), Allen (1941), Hess and Swartz (1941), Jones (1950), Horton (1961), Maitland (1965) and others. Very many factors can affect this availability (Allen, 1941; Maitland, 1965) —including the life cycle of the species of invertebrate concerned. *Ephemerella ignita* is one of the best examples from the Altquhur Burn of how the availability of a single food item may fluctuate, this fluctuation depending almost entirely on its life history. This species of Ephemeroptera is absent from the bottom fauna of the Altquhur Burn from September to March, when it is thought to be in the egg stage (Macan, 1957a). The eggs appear to hatch in April, and by May the species is a common member of the bottom fauna. None are eaten by fish at this time, however, presumably because the nymphs are still very small, i.e. their availability is low not because of their number or habit but because of their size. During June and July there are large numbers of nymphs of medium size, and at this time they become important to the fish (see Maitland, 1965). In August, however, the numbers in the bottom fauna are much lower (due to predation and emergence) and, in spite of the fact that their average size is greater than in previous months, fewer of them are eaten. By September there are only a few large individuals left in the bottom and none are found in the stomachs of fish.

It can be noted from the description of the different species of invertebrates occurring in the Altquhur Burn at station C (see above) that there are very few carnivorous forms present, the main ones being *Rhyacophila*, *Anabolia* and *Polycentropus* (Trichoptera) and *Pentaneura* and *Procladius* (Diptera); none of these was ever common. It appears likely that the main predation on invertebrates here is from those fish present in the stream, and thus specific food relationships

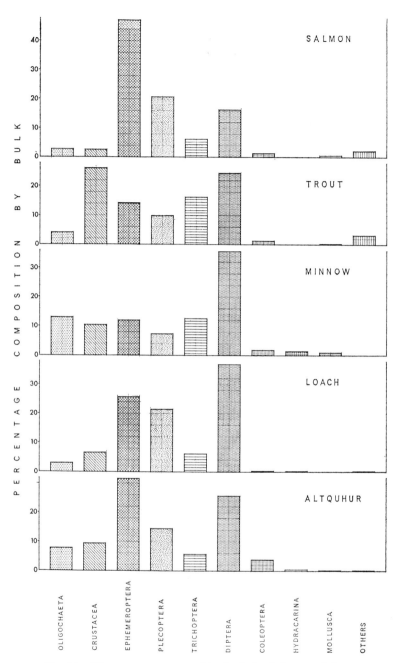

Fig. 14.—The percentage composition by bulk of the aquatic invertebrate food eaten by Salmon, Trout, Minnows and Stone Loach in the
Altquhur Burn during 1961 compared to the average composition of the
bottom fauna of this burn during the same year

such as those discussed above and considered in more detail elsewhere
(Maitland, 1965) are clearly of great importance when trying to assess
the ecological factors affecting this type of community.

The average weight of the total food present in the stomachs of
Salmon, Trout, Minnows and Stone Loach in the Altquhur Burn has
been calculated for four three-monthly periods during 1961, and in
Table 10 these are expressed as percentages of the total body weight
of the fish concerned. In all four species most food was present in

Table 10.—The average amounts of food present in the stomachs of Salmon, Trout,
Minnows, and Stone Loach in the Altquhur Burn during 1961, expressed as a percentage
of the total body weight of the fish concerned (A = Aquatic food, S = Surface food,
N = Number of fish examined). The average weight of bottom fauna (milligrams)
collected in ten minutes (W) is also included

Period	Salmon			Trout			Minnow			Loach			
	A	S	N	A	S	N	A	S	N	A	S	N	W
Jan.–March	1·52	—	15	0·62	0·11	60	0·37	0·14	60	0·89	0·01	40	8·37
April–June	1·75	0·05	12	1·26	0·55	122	0·42	0·14	60	1·73	0·01	60	16·11
July–Sep.	2·51	0·02	61	1·19	1·14	80	0·72	0·14	55	1·91	0·05	60	8·83
Oct.–Dec.	1·49	0·07	52	0·52	0·45	80	0·48	0·17	80	1·26	0·01	44	3·23
Average	1·82	0·04	35	0·90	0·56	86	0·50	0·15	64	1·45	0·02	51	9·14

the stomachs during the summer months and least during the winter
months. This, together with the fact that digestion is much more
rapid at the higher temperatures occurring in summer (Swift, 1961)
indicates that predation on the bottom fauna must be at its peak at
this time. The average amount of food consumed by Salmon, Trout
and Stone Loach was similar, but that consumed by Minnows was
much lower. This low food/body weight ratio may be connected
with the fact that this is the only one of these four species which eats
plant material.

Competition

A definition of competition given by Birch (1957) is that "competition occurs when a number of animals (of the same or different
species) utilize common resources, the supply of which is short; or,
if the resources are not in short supply, competition occurs when the

animals seeking that resource nevertheless harm one another in the process". Andrewartha (1961) considers that the use of the word should be restricted to the first meaning, whilst Brian (1956) divides interspecific competition into two distinct types—Exploitation, "the ability of a species to find, occupy and retain vacant vital resources more easily and quickly than another", and Interference, "the ability of a species to damage another either directly by attacking its individuals or indirectly by harming its resources or blocking its access to them". These two definitions are essentially the same, and, in general, are very useful ones. However, in dealing with the question of competition among fish a somewhat more specific definition is necessary because of the complicated growth/number relationships which occur within fish populations. Maitland (1965) has defined interspecific competition in fish populations as occurring "when the presence of more than one species causes the average total biomass (standing crop) of one of them to be less than it would be if that species were existing alone—species which are directly parasitic or predatory on one another being excepted".

Until a great deal more detailed field work of a quantitative and experimental nature has been carried out on these fish it is impossible to state categorically whether or not competition is occurring among them. At the moment it can be noted that they eat appreciable amounts of the same food organisms, and that food is known to be one of the most important factors limiting growth in fish populations (Brown, 1957). Bottom fauna studies show that this food supply is apparently not a large one, and it would therefore seem probable that there is some degree of competition between Salmon, Trout, Minnows, Stone Loach and Three-spined Sticklebacks in this area. Similar conclusions have also been reached about some of these species by Hartley (1948), Frost (1943), Smyly (1955), Mills (1964), Frost (1950) and others.

VII. Salmon and Trout

As mentioned above, the River Endrick is the most important nursery ground for the Salmon and Trout caught in Loch Lomond and the River Leven, and is moreover important for angling in its own right, being one of the few large unpolluted rivers remaining in the Clyde area. It is clearly impossible to consider the populations of these fish occurring in the River Endrick without discussing too those found in Loch Lomond and the River Leven, and in the present study these waters are treated together. There is no previous account of juvenile Salmon and Trout in this area, though several authors (e.g. Lamond, 1931; Wood, 1954) have discussed adult fish—mainly concerning themselves with fish caught in Loch Lomond.

All the information included here concerning young fish was obtained by the author during a survey of the River Endrick (Maitland, 1963), and also by occasional seine-netting in Loch Lomond and electric fishing in tributary streams other than the River Endrick during 1962 and 1963. Most of the data concerning adult fish are based on the angling returns of members of the Loch Lomond Angling Improvement Association, a body which controls the bulk of the angling in this area. Inevitably such data will have certain limitations, and in general only very broad conclusions can be derived from them; Allen (1951) has shown, however, just how useful such information can be, provided that it is analyzed in the appropriate manner. These returns do not represent all Salmon and Trout taken in the area, for many more are caught by anglers fishing on private waters, by poachers, and by licensed seine-netters in Loch Lomond. It is estimated that the figures given here represent between 40 and 60 per cent of the total annual crop taken by man.

Young Fish

The importance of young Salmon and Trout in the River Endrick has already been stressed, and it was pointed out that they are most abundant in the middle reaches of the river and most tributaries below the Loup of Fintry. The size composition of any one year group is for the most part similar between the two species in any one year, though Salmon do tend to be slightly smaller than Trout (Fig. 12). Because of the greater abundance of Trout in the River Endrick, more detailed information is available about this species than about Salmon; it is clear that the two species have much in common, however. Relatively little work has been carried out on natural populations of young Trout, most of the studies on this species having been concerned with the older stages in rivers and lakes. Frost (1950) has studied the growth and food of young Trout in streams in the north of Scotland, whilst Stuart (1953*b*), Le Cren (1958) and Horton (1961) have all contributed valuable information on stream populations elsewhere in Britain.

In the Altquhur Burn (Fig. 2), adult Trout (both Sea Trout and Brown Trout) were found spawning in the October and November of 1959, 1960 and 1961. Data available for 1961 (Fig. 13) show that the fry started to emerge from the gravel at the beginning of April and continued to do so until the middle of May. The size range of these fry is very small at first, but as summer proceeds a progressively greater disparity appears between the largest and smallest. The most rapid growth of both fry (0+ fish) and parr (1+ fish) takes place between May and August (Fig. 15), this agreeing essentially with the results of Swift (1961) for both hatchery and wild fish. At the end of August the disparity in size between many fry is remarkable, some being over 8 cm. long whilst others are only half that length. The factors responsible for this difference are probably complex, and may be concerned with different hatching times, genetic differences, differences due to chance, and the size hierarchy effect discussed by Brown (1957). Of the larger parr from which scales were examined for age, most were in their second year, though a few older specimens were found—mostly in the deeper pools. It would appear that most

Trout in the Endrick system migrate from the smaller streams to the main river at the end of their second year (cf. Stuart, 1953*b*), and the data in Figs. 13 and 15 would indicate that this migration takes place mainly in April and May, just after the bulk of the fry have hatched.

The results of a length/frequency analysis of populations of young Trout in various tributaries of the River Endrick during August, 1960, and August, 1961, are given in Fig. 16. The general composition of

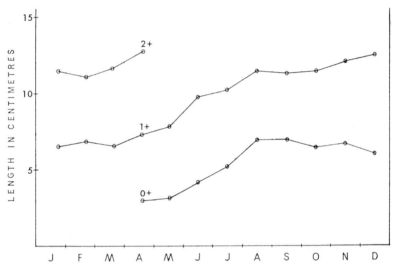

Fig. 15.—The growth of young Trout in the Altquhur Burn during 1961

populations in these tributaries is similar, although in some places the ratio of parr to fry is rather low. It can be seen that the growth of fry varies considerably from one stream to another, and again various inter-related factors of the types mentioned above are presumably responsible. Similar differences between populations of young Trout in becks in England have been noted by Le Cren (1958).

The data obtained for young Salmon in the River Endrick, though of less significance because of the smaller numbers available, show that in general the growth rate and population composition of this species are similar to those of Trout (Fig. 13), and this agrees with the results presented by Frost (1950) and Allen (1940) for this species.

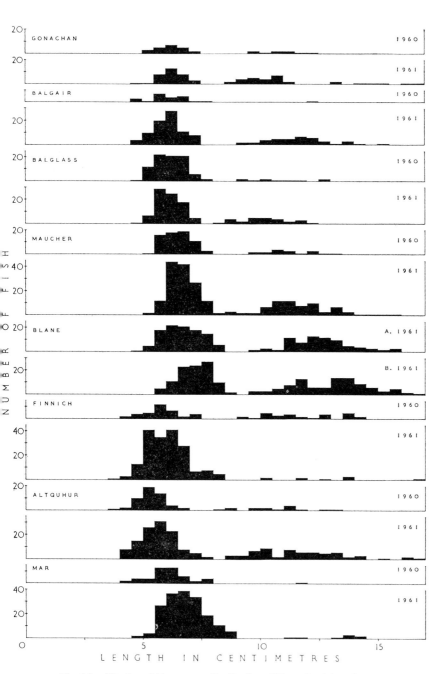

Fig. 16.—The length/frequency distribution of Trout in eight tributary streams in the Endrick system during August 1960 and August 1961. Collections in the Blane Water were made only in 1961: one above the sewage effluent at Blanefield (A), the other below this effluent (B)

129

Food relationships between young fish of the two species have been examined by several workers, and most of the results are in agreement. Alm (1919) was probably the first person to note that Trout appear to eat a higher percentage of surface organisms than Salmon do, and the subsequent work of Frost and Went (1940), Lindroth (1955), Keenleyside (1962), Mills (1964), Maitland (1965) and others have agreed with this finding. The general results of 18 separate samples of the two species taken from the River Endrick in 1961 are shown in Table 11, and it can be seen that in many of these samples the difference is a most marked one. Maitland (1965) has

Table 11.—The amounts of surface food eaten by Salmon and Trout in the Endrick system during 1961, expressed as a percentage of the total amounts by bulk of food eaten

Station	Month	Salmon		Trout	
		Number	% S.F.	Number	% S.F.
Altquhur	Jan.	6	—	20	21·47
Altquhur	Feb.	5	—	20	13·85
Altquhur	March	4	—	20	27·54
Altquhur	April	1	—	40	28·54
Altquhur	May	8	1·60	40	30·94
Altquhur	June	3	7·00	42	32·00
Altquhur	July	21	0·07	40	19·08
Altquhur	August	20	0·12	20	83·34
Altquhur	Sep.	20	1·70	20	44·68
Altquhur	Oct.	20	2·68	20	57·66
Altquhur	Nov.	20	1·15	20	42·60
Altquhur	Dec.	20	10·34	40	41·52
Balglass	August	27	4·16	20	25·49
Drumtian	August	6	—	16	10·62
Mar	August	5	7·67	20	27·96
Maucher	August	18	3·96	20	58·13
Balgair	June	6	8·32	20	68·22
Balgair	August	20	11·41	20	74·16

suggested that the reason for this greater preponderance of surface organisms in the food of Trout, compared to that of Salmon, is that Trout are the more aggressive of the two species (Kalleberg, 1958) and also normally adopt a feeding position in mid-water (Stuart, 1953*b*); they are consequently able to obtain a much greater pro-portion of food falling on to the water surface than Salmon, which are less aggressive and normally lie on or near the bottom in the same stretch of stream. It seems probable that there is competition for both food and territory between the two species, and that a population of either Salmon or Trout would do better in the absence of the other species.

Ratios of Young to Adults

It has already been pointed out that Salmon are much less abundant than Trout in the River Endrick, and in view of the results obtained from the feeding studies described above it is of interest to compare here the relative numbers of these two species as fry and

Table 12.—A comparison of the ratios of Salmon to Trout in the Endrick area. The adults were angled during their spawning migration, whilst the young were collected by handnet

Collection and Year	Salmon		Trout	
	No.	%	No.	%
Adults running: 1958	446	17	2109	83
Young from 1958 spawning (parr): 1960	35	30	80	70
Adults running: 1959	365	14	2157	86
Young from 1959 spawning (fry): 1960	51	23	172	77
(parr): 1961	88	17	415	83
Adults running: 1960	524	13	3505	87
Young from 1960 spawning (fry): 1961	148	12	1038	88
Total Adults 1958–1960	1335	15	7771	85
Total Young 1960–1961	322	16	1705	84

parr in the nursery area with those of the adult fish caught during their spawning migration (the latter figures including fish caught in Loch Lomond and the River Leven, as well as in the River Endrick itself). Table 12 shows that the proportions of Salmon to Trout were similar in the years studied, both among adults and among young fish. The average ratios of adults and young fish during this period correspond very closely indeed, and it would appear that it may well

be possible to predict the proportion of young Salmon to young Trout
in the nursery area by an analysis of the previous seasons' catches of
adult fish, and vice versa.

The average ratio of the numbers of Sea Trout to Brown Trout
caught in the Loch Lomond area from 1959 to 1963 is about 7 to 2.
Though complicated by several factors, such as differences in size
between spawning fish, the presence of resident Brown Trout in
some of the spawning streams, etc., this ratio may give some idea of
the proportions of the two forms in the nursery areas, and thus in the
populations discussed above.

Adult Fish

Other than the analysis of some scales of fish from this area by
Nall (1930), and the annual angling returns reported by Lamond
(1931) and Wood (1954), there is little information available concerning the adult populations of Salmon and Trout in the Loch
Lomond area.

The monthly catches of Salmon, Sea Trout and Brown Trout in
the River Leven, Loch Lomond and the River Endrick for the years
1954 to 1963 inclusive are shown in Figs. 17A, 17B and 17C. It can
be seen that there are certain differences apparent between the data
for the three fish; as few anglers fish specifically for any one of these
fish at any one time it can be assumed that these differences are not,
in fact, artefacts due to angling, but represent differences in the
behaviour of the fish themselves.

Salmon are found commonly in the River Leven from March
onwards and are caught there regularly throughout the fishing season
till October. In Loch Lomond, some fish are caught early in the
year, but most are taken about the middle of the season; whilst in the
River Endrick very few fish are caught early in the year and it is not
until August, September and October that considerable numbers are
taken. The pattern suggested by these angling returns is that the
fish run up the River Leven all during the season, remain in the loch
until the autumn, and then run up the River Endrick (and presumably
other tributary streams also) to spawn.

The returns available for Sea Trout suggest a somewhat different

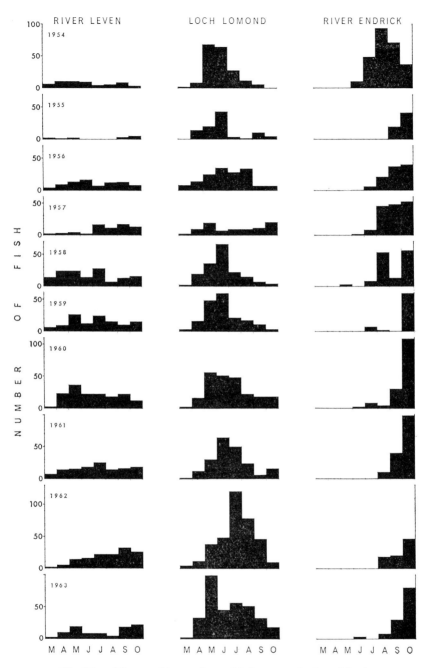

Fig. 17A.—The monthly numbers of Salmon caught from March to October in the River Leven, Loch Lomond and the River Endrick in the years 1954 to 1963

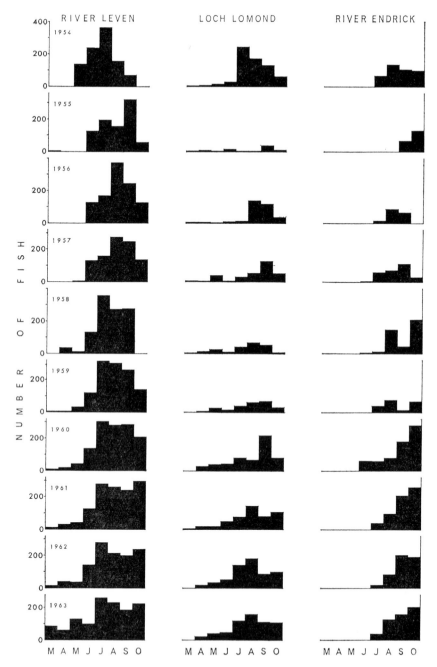

Fig. 17ʙ.—The monthly numbers of Sea Trout caught from March to October in the River Leven, Loch Lomond and the River Endrick in the years 1954 to 1963

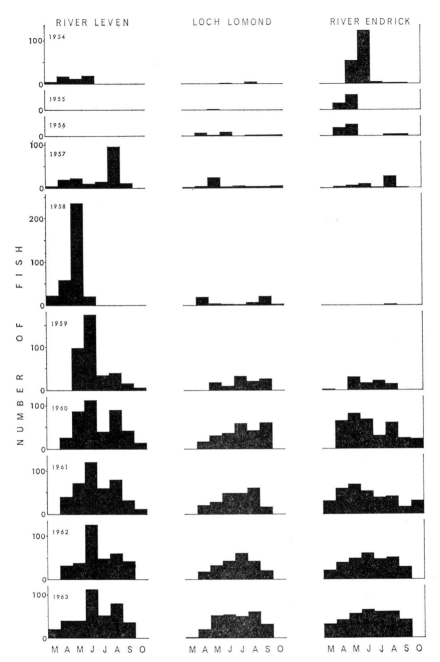

Fig. 17c.—The monthly numbers of Brown Trout caught from March to October in the River Leven, Loch Lomond and the River Endrick in the years 1954 to 1963

behaviour: relatively few fish move up the River Leven in the first part of the season, but in the latter part very many fish are taken. In Loch Lomond small numbers are angled all during the season, but there is never a very noticeable peak in the catch as there is in the River Leven, or as there is with Salmon in the loch. Only in the latter part of the season do Sea Trout occur in numbers in the River Endrick. It would seem probable from these data that Sea Trout mostly move up the River Leven in the second half of the season, disperse in Loch Lomond, and pass quickly into the River Endrick and other tributary streams to spawn.

The angling results for Brown Trout are far less consistent than those for Salmon and Sea Trout, especially between 1954 and 1959; no adequate explanation has yet been found for this variability. From 1959 onwards the numbers taken were much more regular, and, as might be expected, do not show the strong migration patterns found in Salmon and Sea Trout. There are many fish of this species in the River Leven and the River Endrick all the year round, and most of these presumably spawn in their native river. Only fish from Loch Lomond migrate, into the River Endrick and the many other small tributary streams flowing into the loch. It should be noted that the October angling returns are not wholly comparable with those for Salmon and Sea Trout, because the fishing season for Brown Trout ends in the middle of this month, about fifteen days before that of the other two species.

The average weight of the fish caught varies from month to month, and also to some extent from season to season. As is the case with many other British rivers (Jones, 1959), the larger Salmon and Sea Trout are mostly caught early in the year—in March, April and May (Table 13). This is not the case with Brown Trout. The average weight of Salmon caught in the River Leven is normally less than that of those caught in Loch Lomond, but greater than that of those taken in the River Endrick (Table 14). With Sea Trout also the largest fish are taken in Loch Lomond, but with this species the fish angled in the River Endrick are mostly larger than those from the River Leven. The average weight of all fish angled in the River Leven, Loch Lomond and the River Endrick for the 10-year period 1954 to 1963 was 4·19 kg. for Salmon, 0·89 kg. for Sea Trout and 0·35 kg. for

Brown Trout. The fecundity of Salmon is thus greatly increased by their sojourn in the sea, and this is probably an important factor in enabling this species to compete with Trout in areas such as the River Endrick.

Table 13.—The average weight in kilograms of Salmon, Sea Trout and Brown Trout caught in the River Leven, Loch Lomond and the River Endrick from 1954 to 1963

Fish	Mar	Apr	May	Jun	Jul	Aug	Sep	Oct
Salmon								
River Leven	6·51	6·82	5·09	4·52	3·70	4·04	3·97	3·42
Loch Lomond	6·26	6·20	5·58	5·09	4·56	3·74	3·58	4·12
River Endrick	—	—	2·77	4·02	3·41	3·07	3·28	3·62
Sea Trout								
River Leven	0·97	1·15	1·24	0·84	0·77	0·67	0·70	0·64
Loch Lomond	2·95	1·47	1·23	1·15	1·05	0·91	0·89	1·31
River Endrick	—	—	0·45	0·64	0·94	0·92	1·00	0·94
Brown Trout								
River Leven	0·23	0·20	0·26	0·25	0·23	0·19	0·20	0·32
Loch Lomond	1·90	0·45	0·66	0·28	0·45	0·25	0·30	0·48
River Endrick	0·25	0·28	0·25	0·17	0·51	0·41	0·41	1·36

Table 14.—The numbers and average weight in kilograms of Salmon, Sea Trout and Brown Trout caught in the River Leven, Loch Lomond and the River Endrick, from 1954 to 1963

Fish	1954	1955	1956	1957	1958	1959	1960	1961	1962	1963
Salmon										
R. Leven										
Number	57	14	82	65	142	119	159	127	138	90
Ave. Wt.	5·00	4·97	3·85	3·57	4·59	4·67	4·88	4·54	4·20	4·55
L. Lomond										
Number	184	96	158	86	171	178	213	203	354	336
Ave. Wt.	5·42	5·58	4·37	4·79	4·04	5·05	5·15	4·48	4·24	5·04
R. Endrick										
Number	258	60	112	154	133	68	152	148	84	121
Ave. Wt.	3·12	3·65	3·33	2·93	3·22	3·50	3·62	3·00	3·53	3·60
Total										
Number	499	170	352	305	446	365	524	478	576	547
Ave. Wt.	4·49	4·55	3·85	3·76	3·95	4·41	4·55	3·97	3·99	4·39
Sea Trout										
R. Leven										
Number	969	854	1038	926	1081	1169	1292	1310	1144	1274
Ave. Wt.	0·70	0·83	0·76	0·66	0·81	0·72	0·79	0·77	0·74	0·58
L. Lomond										
Number	668	84	329	312	210	236	554	503	610	610
Ave. Wt.	1·05	1·34	0·94	0·95	0·96	0·89	0·81	1·01	1·01	0·91
R. Endrick										
Number	394	196	173	268	414	195	662	606	502	532
Ave. Wt.	0·84	0·96	1·24	1·01	0·93	0·87	0·97	1·06	0·90	0·77
Total										
Number	2031	1134	1540	1506	1705	1600	2508	2419	2256	2416
Ave. Wt.	0·86	1·04	0·98	0·87	0·87	0·83	0·86	0·95	0·88	0·75
Brown Trout										
R. Leven										
Number	51	—	—	176	348	368	411	416	346	380
Ave. Wt.	0·18	—	—	0·35	0·44	0·29	0·16	0·15	0·16	0·15
L. Lomond										
Number	5	1	20	50	54	105	242	220	214	269
Ave. Wt.	0·36	0·45	0·95	0·43	0·37	0·32	0·15	0·17	0·17	0·18
R. Endrick										
Number	183	49	50	48	2	84	344	332	291	356
Ave. Wt.	0·29	0·19	0·62	0·31	1·36	0·30	0·24	0·29	0·16	0·16
Total										
Number	239	50	70	274	404	557	997	968	851	1005
Ave. Wt.	0·21	0·32	0·79	0·43	0·72	0·30	0·18	0·21	0·16	0·16

VIII. THE INFLUENCE OF MAN

There are few areas left in the world today which have not been affected to some degree by the activities of man. The valley of the River Endrick is no exception and man has influenced the ecology of most habitats there in some way: his influence on the river itself is here considered in some detail, especially in connection with the local use of water, which is the main factor affecting the river and its biology.

Water Use

Almost all the water used by man in this region is for domestic purposes. A small distillery and a sand and gravel works are the only industries using water, whilst the rainfall is normally sufficient for agricultural needs. Domestic use is, therefore, the main factor affecting the river, and two aspects of the water used for this purpose are of obvious importance: the initial source of the water which is used to supply the population, and the return to the river (if it has not been piped out of the valley) of this water after use. Its condition at the point of entry to the river is of major importance.

There are ten villages in the area with populations of over 50 (Fig. 18), and these range in size from Milton (population, 64) to Balfron (population, 1250). For the purposes of this study, Killearn Hospital is considered as a separate unit from the village of Killearn itself, mainly becauses it possesses its own sewage works. The remainder of the population, who do not inhabit the villages, are to be found in the many farms and large country houses scattered over the valley, particularly in the middle reaches of the river. The sources of water for these villages have, in the past, been various, but in recent years the position has become much more stable. The present arrangement is shown in Table 15. There are two main sources of water—Carron Reservoir, which supplies most of the

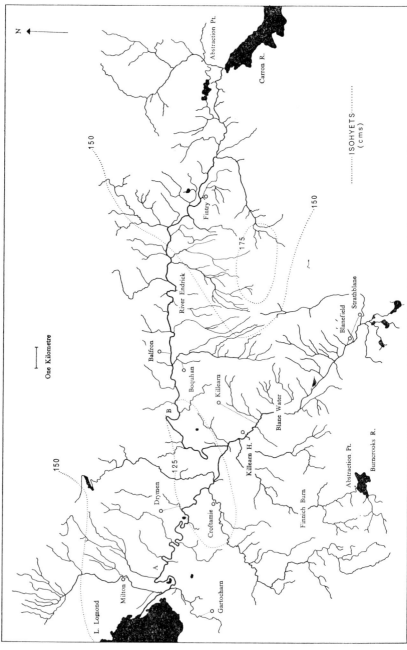

One Kilometre

Fig. 18.—The drainage system of the River Endrick, showing the main villages and points of entry of sewage effluents

Table 15.—Centres of population in the Endrick valley

Village	Pop.	Million Litres of water used per Year	Water Supply	Treatment of Sewage	Hectares of Catchment to Effluent
Gartocharn	114	11	Finlas	Sewage Wks.	373
Croftamie	95	10	Finlas	Septic Tks.	2499
Milton	64	6	Carron	Septic Tks.	1269
Drymen	750	75	Carron	Sewage Wks.	350
Killearn H.	428	43	Carron	Sewage Wks.	4377
Killearn	745	75	Carron	Sewage Wks.	3546
Blanefield	296	30	Carron	Sewage Wks.	1458
Strathblane	670	67	Carron	Sewage Wks.	1458
Boquhan	55	6	Carron	Septic Tks.	800
Balfron	1250	125	Carron	Sewage Wks.	8949
Fintry	260	26	Carron	Sewage Wks.	4605
Rest of pop.	2408	241	Various	Septic Tks.	—

villages in the Stirlingshire portion of the Endrick valley; and Loch Finlas, which supplies those in Dunbartonshire. There are nine lochs within the Endrick watershed, but without exception these are artificial, and, as noted above, were used in the past either for water supplies or to provide power for local mills. The only ones which are in use at the present time (other than for purely local needs) are Burncrooks Reservoir and Carron Reservoir.

Loch Finlas is a reservoir on the Finlas Water, a river flowing into Loch Lomond on the other side of the River Endrick. Any water from this supply is additional to that which is natural to the Endrick catchment. Burncrooks Reservoir, on the other hand, supplies all its water to areas outside the Endrick valley, and all such water is lost to the river. Carron Reservoir has a position intermediate between these two. It lies astride the watershed between the River Endrick and the River Carron, receives water from both catchment areas, and supplies water to both areas. Until recently, only a small part of the Endrick catchment was involved, and as all the compensation was returned just below the point of abstraction the position was a relatively stable one. In 1954, however, a weir (the Endrick Weir) was built across the River Endrick some 6 km. below its source, and the water from this additional catchment area of 1787 hectares is now abstracted into Carron Reservoir. All the figures given here referring to the abstraction into Carron Reservoir are for this new abstraction, and do not include the small abstraction which was taking place before 1954.

Figures relating to this system of water supply are shown in Table 16. Because the amount of water which is abstracted varies with rainfall, it is difficult to give accurate average figures of the gain

Table 16.—Water abstracted and supplied (in millions of litres) in the Endrick catchment area in 1960

Water Supply	Volume Abstracted	Volume Supplied
Loch Finlas	0·0	17·55
Carron Reservoir	5561·03	283·58
Burncrooks Reservoir	1868·04	0·0

Total loss to Endrick catchment area in 1960: 7127·94 million litres

and loss to the Endrick system. Those figures which are given in Table 16 are based on information available for 1960, and as this was a fairly average year as far as rainfall is concerned (Figs. 7 and 19), they should not be too atypical. It can be seen that there was an annual loss of over 7,000 million litres of water to the River Endrick, and as almost all the abstraction took place near the headwaters of the river, any effect would be felt along its entire length. That water which is additional to the Endrick catchment is received near the mouth of the river and is therefore of little value.

All the water from the villages in the valley, together with the domestic sewage with which it is now mixed, passes into the River Endrick or one of its tributaries. In all cases there is some form of treatment before this sewage enters the river, and in general the standard of effluent entering the river would appear to be good. An analysis of the effluent from one of the newer sewage works (Drymen) is included in Table 17. Most of the larger villages have modern sewage works consisting of grit chambers, settling tanks and filter beds. The worst effluent until recently was probably that from Balfron, where the works before 1962 consisted only of a grit chamber

Table 17.—Chemical analyses (in milligrams per litre) of water from the River Endrick near Balfron (5th February, 1951) and from the Drymen Sewage Works (25th January, 1960)

	(i) 20 metres below Balfron Effluent	(ii) 40 metres below Balfron Effluent	(iii) 500 metres below Balfron Effluent	(iv) Drymen Sewage	(v) Drymen Effluent
Suspended Solids	1	1	1	69	32
Dissolved Solids	70	90	80	240	240
Chloride (as Cl)	11	11	11	36	35
Alkalinity (as $CaCO_3$)	25	27	29	153	77
Ammoniacal Nitrogen	0·02	0·41	0·06	17·6	6·6
Albuminoid Nitrogen	0·06	0·14	0·09	7·9	1·2
Nitric Nitrogen	trace	trace	trace	nil	8·4
Dissolved Oxygen	8·8	8·9	8·5	nil	3·9
B.O.D.	1·7	5·6	2·4	90·0	16·0
O_2 absorbed from K MnO_4 in 4 hours	1·8	2·7	2·0	25·6	9·8

and settling tanks. A new sewage works has now been constructed here, however, which is capable of giving the sewage a much more efficient treatment. The smaller villages have individual septic tanks, whose effluent either passes into the nearest water course or direct to the main river. Outwith the villages, most farms and private houses in the area have individual septic tanks.

Abstraction

It is difficult to assess the exact effect of abstraction on a river, except where total abstraction is taking place. Where this occurs the results are obvious. More often, however, there is only partial abstraction, and this is the case with the greater part of the River Endrick. In such cases there will obviously be variation from one part of the river to another, and at any one place the effect will vary with the weather.

As described above there are two areas of abstraction within the Endrick valley. The area abstracted into Burncrooks Reservoir is small (440 hectares) and is less than 2 per cent of the total Endrick catchment area. The compensation water is reasonable (2·83 million litres per day, which is 33 per cent of the gross yield); moreover this is discharged just below the point of abstraction. As mentioned above, the situation at Carron Reservoir was similar to this until 1954, but the new abstraction takes in an additional area of 1782 hectares (over 6 per cent of the Endrick catchment area) and includes the entire headwaters of the main river. Some of the effects of this abstraction are immediate and obvious; others may occur only from time to time, be more dependent on the weather and be less obvious, though none the less important. Full details concerning this abstraction have been discussed elsewhere (Maitland, 1962*b*), the effect on the river immediately below the point of abstraction being a marked one.

Below Randieford Weir, where the compensation water from Carron Reservoir enters, the river recovers somewhat, and during the summer a larger area of its rocky bed is permanently covered by flowing water. The effect of the abstraction here, and further downstream, is difficult to assess, since little information is available as to the state of the river before the abstraction took place. Some idea of the variation in flow at this point can be gained by examining the relevant data for 1960, shown in Fig. 19. Here, the average monthly flow at the Endrick Weir (aqueduct), i.e. the water which was abstracted (the figures shown are corrected to allow for the compensation water which was returned downstream), and also at the Randieford Weir, i.e. the water which passed downstream, are given, as well as the monthly rainfall at Fintry and the average monthly water levels at station A (Woodend) and station B (Drumtian). It can be seen that the main abstraction took place during the summer months when the water levels in the river were at their lowest; and that during the winter months, when water levels in the river were at their highest, practically no abstraction took place. At Randieford Weir during the summer the flow rarely rose much above the minimum necessary for compensation, except after very heavy rain; whilst during the winter the flow was very much greater. This variation in flow must obviously produce effects in the river below. In the lower stretches of the river the results of quantitative studies have indicated that heavy spates may have a disastrous effect on the fauna (Fig. 10), scouring the river bed and reducing the numbers of many species

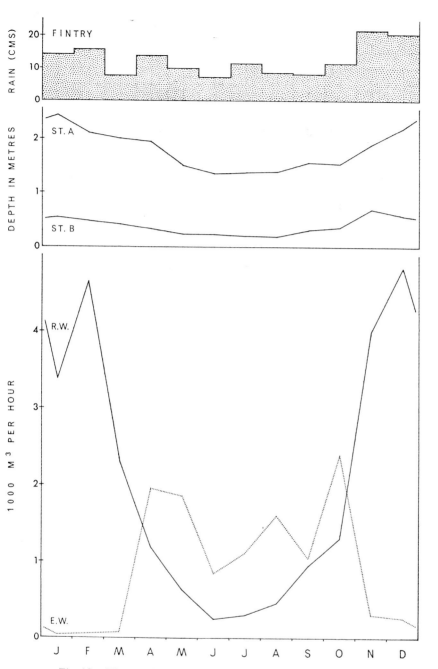

Fig. 19.—The monthly rainfall at Fintry, the water levels at station A (Woodend) and station B (Drumtian) and the flows at Randieford Weir (R.W.) and Endrick weir (E.W.) during 1960

145

very considerably. In the upper stretches, where the flow in summer is now much less than formerly, the river bed may still be subjected to spates which are just as large as those which occurred here before, because of the nature of the abstraction. It is difficult for the river bed to stabilize under such conditions, and at times the loss of bottom fauna must be considerable.

As noted elsewhere, the River Endrick is one of the few Salmon rivers left in the Clyde area, and in addition its waters act as a nursery ground for most of the Salmon caught in the River Leven and Loch Lomond. Abstraction of water from the river may be particularly dangerous to salmonids during their period of egg development: redds in shallow water which were formerly productive may now be less so, for though still the same to fish during the high water of the spawning season, if thereafter a dry period occurs the lowered water level may kill the developing eggs. Even though the redds may not dry out completely, damage can still be done by the reduction of the necessary flow through the gravel (Stuart, 1953*a*), and the increased chance of silting caused by this reduction of flow, which may also kill the eggs (Stuart, 1953*b*). This is likely to happen only if there is a considerable amount of abstraction in the early part of the year.

Land Development

The only large bodies of standing water in the Endrick valley are the nine lochs mentioned above, all of which are artificial. The effects of such reservoirs on a river system are various, but mostly beneficial. The result of building an obstruction in the form of a dam across a tributary valley is immediate and obvious locally, and the fauna of the resulting reservoir undergoes a rapid change from a lotic to a lentic community, which may take some years to stabilize. The effect of such reservoirs is not only local, however, and changes may take place in the river below; thus the outflow from such a body of water contains much larger amounts of plankton than the original stream normally would (Brook and Woodward, 1956), and some invertebrate species may be commoner in the river as a result (Badcock, 1953*b*; Hynes, 1959). Lochs also exert a stabilizing influence on a river system, as has been shown by McLean (1940), and fluctuations in water level are less violent as a result.

The influence of land drainage on rivers has recently been discussed by Stuart (1959). Only in a few places in the Endrick valley, however, has the river bed been altered for the improvement of drainage, though large areas of the land have been piped or ditched to provide better drainage for agricultural purposes. This has increased the dangers resulting from higher water levels in wet weather and lower water levels in dry weather—both a direct result of the faster run-off of water from the land. Areas of forest tend to offset such effects (Rothacher, 1953), as well as practically eliminating soil erosion, and the forests recently planted near Carron and Drymen will no doubt be of considerable value to the river in future years.

The most probable damage done to the river by local industry is by the working of sand and gravel which is carried out near Drymen. Here, the hillside consists of alternate layers of sand, gravel and clay (Jack, 1877), and these are at present being worked and removed. Washings from this quarry pass into the Drymen Burn some 600 m. above its junction with the River Endrick, and only 300 m. above the outflow of the Drymen sewage effluent. The effect of sand pit washings on local fauna has been studied by Hamilton (1961), who carried out his investigations on the River Fruin, another of the streams flowing into Loch Lomond. He concludes that such washings involve little danger to the invertebrate fauna and fish, unless large amounts of sand settle out and silt over the substrate of the stream. The spawning of salmonids is almost certainly affected if such silt is present in any quantity, because of the effect which it has on their eggs (Stuart, 1953*b*). In the Drymen Burn there is some evidence of the increased settlement of sand below the quarry, but owing to the fact that the streams in this area have much larger amounts of sand and gravel in their beds normally than do other tributary streams in the Endrick valley (Maitland, 1962*a*), the effect of this is probably small. Moreover, the fact that only a short stretch of the stream is affected, together with the fact that half of this stretch carries a fair amount of sewage anyway, does not prevent spawning from being carried out successfully in this burn in the reaches above the silted stretch (which form in fact the greater part of its length), even if the silting here were serious. As far as the main river is concerned, below the Drymen Burn the current is slow, and, except in the few stretches of riffle which occur between here and the mouth, the natural river bed is composed of sand. Further silting, therefore, due to sand washings, is likely to have little effect.

The only other quarry at present being worked in the area is in the Blane valley, where a local outcrop of rock is quarried for road metal. Washings from a dump beside this quarry are small and, other than local silting in a small burn, the effect on the river is slight. A small distillery in the Blane valley has been the cause of intermittent pollution of the Blane Water, and during recent years the occurrence of large numbers of dead fish here has almost certainly been due to the discharge from this distillery. Measures have now been taken by the proprietors to prevent recurrences of this pollution.

Sewage

In the case of sewage, the position is in some ways simpler, for by taking samples of the fauna from similar stations above and below the discharge of sewage effluents it is possible to discover what effect the effluent is having upon the fauna of the stream (Hynes, 1960). The general appearance of the River Endrick, as regards pollution, is good. Other than during spates (when the water colours a rich reddish-brown), the river water is fairly clear down to its junction with the Blane Water, and the substrate can normally be seen clearly at a depth of one metre, often more. The appearance of the Blane Water is less satisfactory, almost certainly due to the large amount of sewage, relative to its flow, which it must carry, compared to the main river (Fig. 18, Table 18). In the Blane Water, below the point of entry of the Killearn effluent, the water is slightly turbid at all times of the year, whilst between the Killearn Hospital effluent discharge and the main river, the water may take on a milky appearance. The fauna of these stretches, however, still has a varied composition, though some groups are clearly affected. The increase in turbidity may affect the growth of algae in the river at this point (though there is no direct evidence to this effect) by cutting down the light which is available, but some of the higher plants are certainly not affected

Table 18.—Chemical analyses (in milligrams per litre) of water from five
stations in the Blane Water on 5th February, 1962

	(i) 3 kilos above Blanefield Effluent	(ii) 200 metres above Blanefield Effluent	(iii) 200 metres below Blanefield Effluent	(iv) 100 metres below Killearn Effluent	(v) 2 kilos below Killearn Effluent
Temperature (°C)	4·0	6·0	6·0	6·5	6·5
pH	7·3	7·2	7·2	7·2	7·2
Suspended Solids	1	3	8	13	8
Chloride (as Cl)	11	11	11	12	12
Alkalinity (as $CaCO_3$)	35	35	35	45	50
Ammoniacal Nitrogen	nil	nil	trace	0·16	0·16
Albuminoid Nitrogen	nil	trace	trace	0·08	0·09
Nitrous Nitrogen	nil	trace	trace	trace	trace
Nitric Nitrogen	nil	0·12	0·12	0·33	0·33
Dissolved Oxygen	12·9	12·5	12·6	12·5	12·1
% Sat. Diss. Oxygen	101·6	103·7	104·5	104·9	101·6
B.O.D.	1·7	2·0	3·1	2·4	1·7

adversely, for it is here that some of the most luxuriant growths to
be found in the whole river system occur (see below). Below its
junction with the Blane Water, the water in the main river is almost
always slightly turbid, and this, combined with the fact that the depth
from here on gradually increases, means that only occasionally can
the substrate be seen between here and the mouth.

Visual observation of the macroflora of the River Endrick indicates
that it is greatly influenced in some places by sewage effluents. In
the main river, above its junction with the Blane Water, there are no
large growths of any Angiosperm species other than *Myriophyllum
alterniflorum*, which is common in most parts of the river system
(Fig. 3). In the Blane Water, however, starting below the Killearn
effluent, and continuing downstream for several miles (including the
main river), luxuriant growths of several species occur, particularly
Elodea canadensis and *Potamogeton crispus*. The latter species especially covers large areas of the river bed in some places. Large growths
such as these have been noted by other workers in streams subjected
to mild organic pollution (Hynes, 1960), and they are assumed to be
a direct result of the fertilizing effect of the effluent, together with

the increased silting which it brings about. Such growths must clearly affect the local fauna to a marked extent, not only by providing food and shelter directly, but also by the further increase in silting which takes place round their lower stems and root systems. Other effects caused by such growths are discussed by Westlake (1959). During the present survey, both in the Blane Water and in the main river below, these weed beds have been found to support a rich and varied fauna, including particularly Crustacea and Mollusca, few species of which are really abundant elsewhere in the river. Of the fish, the Three-spined Stickleback (*Gasterosteus aculeatus*) seems to be favoured by these weed beds, and they possibly offer this species its optimum habitat in the River Endrick.

Stations examined

For the purpose of studying the effect of local sewage effluents on the fauna of the River Endrick, the following two regions were selected: (1) the stretch where the sewage effluent from Balfron was discharged, and where at the time of study the sewage was only crudely treated before being passed into the river; (2) the stretch where the sewage effluent from the Blanefield sewage works was discharged, this works being one of the most recent in the area and serving both Blanefield and Strathblane. Further information about these two effluents and the villages which discharge them is given in Table 15. At both these places, stations were selected which were as similar as possible regarding substrate, current, depth, etc. Three stations were chosen at each place, as follows: (a) 20 m. above the effluent, (b) 20 m. below the effluent, (c) 200 m. below the effluent. At all stations the current was fast (approximately 30 cm./sec. at Balfron, and 45 cm./sec. at Blanefield), and the river bed was composed of small stones with some gravel. Trees (mostly Alder) overhung the water at both places. At Balfron the river was some 18 m. across, and at the times of sampling the water depth varied from 30 to 50 cm. At Blanefield, the river was only 5 m. across, and the water depth varied from 20 to 40 cm. at the times of sampling. It can be seen from Fig. 18 that, other than local drainage from septic tanks, there were no sewage effluents entering the river above either site.

At Balfron, samples of the bottom fauna were taken with a hand-

net 40 cm. in diameter, and with a mesh of 16 threads per cm.
Collecting was done in a similar fashion to that advocated by Macan
(1958), stones and gravel being moved about and rubbed by hand in
front of the net in order to dislodge animals which were then washed
by the current into the net. Each collection was taken for a standard
period of ten minutes, and during 1961 three series of collections
were taken: one in February, one in June and one in October, in
order to include those animals whose populations undergo large
seasonal variation (e.g. *Ephemerella ignita*).

At Blanefield, a series of samples similar to the above was taken
in June only, and at this time an additional station was included:
(d) 400 metres below the Killearn Hospital effluent. In February
instead, a series of quantitative samples was taken by means of the
shovel sampler described elsewhere (Maitland, 1964*a*), which sampled
an area of 552 cm^2 to a depth of 12 cm. The net used had a mesh of
65 threads per cm., and three separate samples were taken from the
river bed at each station (i.e. nine samples in all).

In the field, all samples were placed in individual plastic bags,
labelled, and 5 per cent formalin was added. In the laboratory the
samples were washed in a circular metal sieve (16 meshes per cm.),
and then sorted by eye in a shallow glass dish, first over a black background, then over a white one. With the shovel samples, the material
passing through the 16 mesh per cm. sieve was collected and washed
in a finer sieve (65 meshes per cm.), and then sorted in a shallow
maze-type plastic dish under the low power of a binocular microscope. Finally, all the animals sorted from the samples were identified,
as far as was practicable, and counted.

The condition of the river bed in the vicinity of both effluents
varied from time to time, and the appearance of the substrate at each
station at the times of sampling is shown elsewhere (Maitland, 1962*b*).
Directly below each effluent, on that side on which it entered, there
was a development of sewage fungus and silt which gradually extended across the river and then disappeared. The extent of this zone
varied from month to month, but was usually at its greatest during
the summer. The effluent at both Balfron and Blanefield was cloudy
white in colour and gave the river water below a slightly turbid
appearance for some distance. No chemical tests were carried out

on the river water at the time of sampling, though some relevant analyses can be seen in Table 18.

The effect of the sewage on fish, below these and other effluents in the river, appears to be small, though the river bed for some distance below each has been rendered useless for salmonids to spawn in because of the growth of sewage fungus, which, as Rasmussen (1955) has shown, prevents Trout eggs from developing. At Balfron, Salmon (*Salmo salar*), Trout (*Salmo trutta*), Minnow (*Phoxinus phoxinus*) and Stone Loach (*Nemacheilus barbatula*) are common both above and below the effluent at all times of the year. At Blanefield, Salmon and Trout are the only common fish, and here too they occur both above and below the effluent throughout the year. Indeed, it appeared from visual observation here that the numbers of fish below the effluent were higher than was usual in the river, and it was suspected that this may have been due to the sewage. Such a situation has been found in other rivers (Hynes, 1960), but unfortunately it was impossible to carry out quantitative sampling of the fish population here. Qualitative sampling was carried out, however, and all fish caught were measured before they were released. Two samples were taken, one from a short stretch of the river some distance above the effluent, the other from a similar stretch below. The results for Trout are included in Fig. 16, and though both fry and parr below the effluent showed greater average length than those above (7·3 and 13·1 cm. respectively below, and 6·7 and 12·6 cm. above), as has been found with other species in the Trent (Butcher, 1959), the difference is not sufficient to be of great significance. There is little evidence, either, of a difference in population composition, for both Salmon and Trout were taken commonly above and below the effluent.

Results

As far as organic pollution is concerned, the worst dangers in the Endrick system were almost certainly on the main river at Balfron, and on the Blane Water, below the effluents from Blanefield and Strathblane, Killearn and Killearn Hospital. It can be seen, however, that even at these places (Tables 19 and 20), unless extreme conditions prevail—such as a deterioration in the condition of one of the effluents or an unusually long period of hot, dry weather—the danger to the

Table 19.—Percentage composition of the invertebrate fauna in the River Endrick near the Balfron sewage effluent (1961)

Fauna	February			June			October		
	(a)	(b)	(c)	(a)	(b)	(c)	(a)	(b)	(c)
Naididae	17·9	7·2	51·1	1·1	0·9	1·5	0·9	5·6	10·5
Tubificidae	2·5	26·0	19·3	0·6	77·0	0·5	0·4	60·0	14·8
Lumbriculidae	5·8	0·4	0·9	0·2	0·9	3·4	4·3	1·0	6·0
Gammarus pulex	0·1	0·3	0·1	0·2	0·1	0·1	2·7	0·8	1·6
Caenis rivulorum	5·5	0·1	0·6	1·7	—	0·5	20·3	0·1	2·1
Caenis macrura	0·6	0·1	0·1	0·8	—	0·3	—	—	—
Ephemerella ignita	—	—	—	18·3	0·3	10·7	0·1	—	0·4
Ecdyonurus venosus	0·8	—	0·1	1·4	—	0·2	1·4	—	0·6
Rhithrogena semicolorata	1·5	—	0·4	—	—	—	1·0	—	0·2
Baetis pumilus	3·1	—	0·2	—	—	—	0·1	—	—
Baetis rhodani	6·2	0·8	8·7	1·5	0·1	0·6	0·4	—	4·4
Leuctra fusca	—	—	—	6·8	—	0·3	—	—	—
Other Plecoptera	3·0	0·1	0·3	0·1	—	0·1	1·9	0·1	0·6
Hydropsyche instabilis	0·3	0·1	0·1	0·1	—	0·1	1·2	—	1·3
Polycentropus flavomaculatus	0·6	0·4	0·1	0·1	—	—	6·9	1·0	1·5
Rhyacophila dorsalis	—	—	—	0·1	—	0·1	—	—	0·5
Agapetus fuscipes	—	—	—	1·5	—	0·1	—	—	—
Hydroptila forcipata	—	0·1	—	0·5	—	0·1	—	—	—
Simulium ornatum	0·9	0·6	0·6	—	—	—	0·2	0·1	0·7
Simulium reptans	—	—	—	0·1	—	0·3	—	—	—
Ceratopogonidae	5·7	0·2	2·2	0·1	—	0·2	0·3	0·1	1·4
Tanypodinae	3·0	6·3	0·7	6·8	2·6	5·2	3·6	1·2	1·7
Chironominae	0·8	3·2	0·5	4·5	2·9	2·5	1·3	2·4	0·9
Diamesinae	0·1	1·0	0·1	0·1	5·3	0·1	0·1	4·1	0·2
Orthocladiinae	27·0	51·1	11·0	46·3	9·6	70·8	21·0	21·8	30·5
Helmis maugei	0·6	0·3	0·1	0·1	—	0·1	1·7	0·1	0·8
Esolus parallelopipedus	9·1	0·4	1·4	3·7	—	0·5	14·7	0·1	7·4
Limnius tuberculatus	0·4	0·5	0·2	0·1	—	0·1	3·9	0·3	2·0
Latelmis volkmari	1·5	0·1	0·4	0·9	—	0·6	4·4	0·1	4·4
Hydracarina	0·8	0·1	0·2	1·6	—	0·1	2·9	0·1	2·5
Ancylus fluviatilis	0·6	0·3	0·4	0·2	—	0·1	0·5	0·1	0·4
Others	1·6	0·3	0·2	0·5	0·3	0·8	3·8	0·9	2·6
Total number in sample	1849	1953	6836	4980	874	5932	959	1467	2125

fauna as a whole, particularly the fish, is small. As noted below, since the time of sampling (1961) a new sewage works has been installed to serve Balfron, and this means that the greatest effects from organic pollution will now be found in the Blane Water.

These sewage effluents do have a marked effect on the invertebrate fauna of the river, however, particularly in the stretches just

Table 20A.—Density of the invertebrate fauna per square
metre in the Blane Water near the Blanefield sewage
effluent (February, 1961)

Fauna	(a)	(b)	(c)
Naididae	695	1419	628
Tubificidae	187	2072	598
Lumbriculidae	60	109	24
Enchytraeidae	24	36	6
Erpobdella octoculata	12	—	36
Harpacticoidea	1709	453	412
Gammarus pulex	6	6	12
Ecdyonurus torrentis	12	18	18
Rhithrogena semicolorata	12	12	60
Baetis pumilus	36	24	60
Baetis rhodani	1033	308	930
Brachyptera risi	48	6	36
Amphinemura sulcicollis	42	91	109
Leuctra inermis	332	906	454
Chloroperla torrentium	18	18	36
Hydropsyche instabilis	—	—	18
Polycentropus flavomaculatus	24	24	42
Rhyacophila dorsalis	36	18	85
Simulium ornatum	24	—	48
Simulium reptans	54	12	85
Tanypodinae	85	157	163
Chironominae	1039	719	906
Orthocladiinae	2652	5442	15932
Helmis maugei	12	6	24
Esolus parallelopipedus	54	48	103
Latelmis volkmari	—	12	12
Hydracarina	72	30	115
Ancylus fluviatilis	109	—	60
Nematoda	145	266	586
Others	163	115	483
Total	8695	12327	22081

below their points of entry. At both places which were studied, the general effect of the sewage was first to induce a large increase in the numbers of Tubificidae present and a reduction in the numbers of most other species. This effect is similar to that found by other workers (Hynes, 1960), though the population here was perhaps unusual in that relatively few *Chironomus* sp., which are normally favoured by this type of pollution (Butcher, 1959), were present. Gradually below this stretch there was a return to the normal fauna; small green Orthocladiinae larvae were particularly common at first,

Table 20B.—Percentage composition of the invertebrate fauna in the Blane Water near the Blanefield sewage effluent (June, 1961)

Fauna	(a)	(b)	(c)	(d)
Naididae	1·3	5·6	0·6	1·7
Tubificidae	1·1	5·5	4·5	30·0
Lumbriculidae	0·3	0·8	0·3	2·3
Erpobdella octoculata	0·1	0·1	0·3	0·5
Gammarus pulex	0·2	0·1	0·5	0·1
Asellus aquaticus	—	—	—	0·1
Ephemerella ignita	14·8	1·9	5·8	6·7
Ecdyonurus torrentis	0·6	—	0·5	2·1
Baetis rhodani	2·9	0·4	1·8	0·8
Leuctra fusca	28·3	0·2	22·0	2·5
Other Plecoptera	0·1	—	0·3	—
Hydropsyche instabilis	0·1	—	0·2	—
Polycentropus flavomaculatus	0·4	0·2	1·5	—
Rhyacophila dorsalis	1·1	0·7	1·5	0·1
Agapetus fuscipes	2·5	2·9	0·9	—
Hydroptila sp.	0·4	0·5	0·1	—
Simulium ornatum	1·6	0·5	0·2	—
Simulium reptans	6·3	0·7	0·3	—
Tanypodinae	3·0	2·9	2·2	0·8
Chironominae	1·1	1·6	7·4	3·5
Diamesinae	0·1	1·3	0·3	0·2
Orthocladiinae	30·6	73·3	46·3	45·8
Helmis maugei	0·1	0·1	0·3	0·1
Esolus parallelopipedus	1·6	0·2	0·2	0·1
Latelmis volkmari	0·1	0·1	0·2	0·3
Hydracarina	0·2	0·1	—	0·9
Ancylus fluviatilis	0·1	—	0·6	—
Others	1·0	0·3	1·2	1·4
Total number in sample	3605	4776	4800	4449

the density being normally greatly in excess of that found above the effluent. The numbers of several other species too, as they recovered, tended to be higher than those above the effluent.

Dense populations of Tubificidae are always found to occur in areas where the normally clean rocky substrate is thickly covered by silt and sewage fungus. This zone never extends far, however, and the substrate rapidly becomes cleaner as one passes downstream from the effluent. At Balfron, where the maximum development of sewage fungus in the entire river system occurred, it was in fact only

11

rarely that the zone extended right across the river. Normally it started as a narrow belt running along the right side of the river below the discharge of the sewage effluent (Plate VIв), this belt gradually broadening out across the river as the cloudy water of the effluent mixed with the clear river water. However, as the belt of sewage fungus became broader, so did it become less intense, and only a few hundred metres below the effluent it disappeared altogether. Thus, at its maximum, this zone of sewage fungus and silt was only a stretch varying in breadth from 2 to 10 m. which extended for some 500 m. along the river. This maximum was reached during the summer months. During the rest of the year the zone was smaller, for much of the sewage fungus and silt tended to be washed away at this time by spates (cf. Fig. 10). At Blanefield, the current is swifter in the region of the effluent discharge, minimizing its effect, and there was never a great development of sewage fungus and silt of the type observed at Balfron. Some growth of sewage fungus was evident, however, particularly under stones and in quieter water, for a maximum distance of 200 m. below the effluent in summer.

These results have been considered in detail elsewhere (Maitland, 1962*b*) where the effect of the sewage on the ecology of common invertebrate species is fully discussed. In general, it can be seen that the effect of the sewage on the invertebrate fauna at both Balfron (Table 19) and Blanefield (Table 20) was similar, and resembles that found by other workers in rivers where mild organic pollution occurs (Harrison and Elsworth, 1958; Hynes, 1960; etc.). Such differences as there are between the two places are almost certainly caused by the differences in the quality of the effluents and the speed of the current just below their point of entry to the river. Thus at Balfron the effluent, which had undergone no filtration, passed out into the river where the current was slow enough to allow much of the silt to settle out and cover the rocks. Sewage fungus developed here too, and the current was moderate enough to allow a fairly luxuriant growth, which, as it developed, trapped more silt. At Blanefield the effluent, which was smaller and had passed through modern filter beds, was discharged into the river at a point where the swifter current prevented much silt from settling out and also restricted the growth of sewage fungus on the river bed. Thus burrowing forms such as Tubificidae and *Prodiamesa olivacea*, which are common in the sewage fungus zone at Balfron, were reduced in number or even absent here.

Conversely, forms such as *Agapetus fuscipes* (and possibly *Leuctra fusca* and *L. inermis*), which were apparently unable to withstand the silt and thick sewage fungus at Balfron and were therefore absent from the sewage fungus zone there, occurred in this zone at Blanefield. Some were in fact favoured by it here, probably finding an increased food supply without the accompanying disadvantage of heavy silting.

The results of the present study indicate that whilst the sewage effluents from villages in the Endrick valley do have an effect on the invertebrate fauna of the river, extreme changes, when they do occur, are very local, and take place just below the point of entry of the effluent. After this the fauna rapidly recovers, and the main effect of the effluent is one of slight fertilization. Fish appear to be affected little, and probably benefit from an increase in their food supply. No cases of fish dying as a result of discharge of domestic sewage are known from the River Endrick; and, even if conditions were to become worse for short periods, most of the species concerned are mobile and could swim upstream or into local tributaries until conditions improved. If the conditions were much worse for long periods, however, or if toxic substances were introduced into the effluent (or added to the river water elsewhere, for that matter, as regularly happens when poachers are working on the river), then the results could be very serious for the fish stocks. Probably the worst case of this type which has occurred in the River Endrick was in 1930, when the discharge from the creosote tank in a saw-mill entered the river and did extensive damage to the fish below its point of entry (Lamond, 1931).

The chemical results which are available for the river (Tables 5, 18 and 21) show that the oxygen content of the water in most places is high—even below many of the sewage effluents. The only high B.O.D.s ever found have been from just below the discharge from the old sewage works at Balfron. It would appear that the immediate effect of sewage on the invertebrate fauna is due more to the influence of silt and sewage fungus than to a lack of oxygen in the water. The results discussed above are in agreement with this: as the silted appearance of the substrate disappears so does the normal fauna reappear.

It is more difficult to assess the effect on the fauna of the river of man's interference in other ways. Apart from the upper reaches, where the abstraction may be great, the invertebrate fauna appears at the moment to be relatively unaffected by local water use, and compares favourably with that of other clean rivers which have been studied in Europe and in America. This desirable state is obviously one which all concerned should endeavour to maintain—especially, perhaps, because of the importance of the River Endrick as a nursery ground for game fish.

Future Changes

It would seem reasonable to consider, finally, man's future plans for water use in the Endrick valley, and to attempt to assess their subsequent effect on the fauna of the river. With a few exceptions, the outlook appears to be a favourable one. There are no major changes anticipated in the water supply to the region in the near future, and the position is likely to be a stable one for some time. Though no further abstraction is envisaged in the Carron area, there is a proposed development of a further 400 hectares of gathering ground at Burncrooks Reservoir in the future. This will almost double the area which is abstracted from here at present, and will further reduce the flow of water in the Catter and the Finnich Burns, both of which are important nursery streams in the Endrick system (Fig. 2). The worst danger from sewage was probably at Balfron, but as a new modern sewage works has now been provided here the position should be better in the future. A new sewage works is also being provided at Fintry and a larger one planned for Killearn, and these too should help to improve the quality of the river water even further. As far as can be ascertained, there is little planned for the area in the way of development; and in both the Clyde Valley Planning Report and the Stirlingshire Planning Report it is proposed to develop the valley as a regional recreational area and maintain it as a rural area (Hunter, 1960). What little change is going on at present mainly involves the building of private houses on the outskirts of the existing villages, and the replacement of older houses within the villages.

The recently proposed Mid Scotland Scheme, for taking some 454 million litres per day from Loch Lomond and piping it across the Endrick valley to the Forth catchment area, may have far reaching effects on the River Endrick. This scheme as it was first envisaged involves the building of a weir across the River Leven where it leaves Loch Lomond in order to raise the mean annual level of the loch by about 60 cm. This weir may possibly affect the passage of migratory fish from the River Leven into Loch Lomond and the River Endrick, and vice versa; and also the higher average level of the loch may increase the danger of flooding in the lower reaches of the River Endrick, much of which is already subject to flooding during spates.

Proposals have recently been made, too, concerning the building of a new town at Finnich Toll in the Endrick valley. This town would be situated near the Finnich Burn, less than a mile from its junction with the Blane Water. The population envisaged is 10,000, and it is obvious that such a scheme would have an important effect on the Endrick valley, the total population of which is at present just over 7000. The main aspects affecting the fauna of the river, as is the case with the villages at present in the area, are the problems concerned with water supply and sewage disposal. The provision of water would probably involve further abstraction of water from the Kilpatrick Hills, and the subsequent effect of this would presumably be felt in the tributary burns running into the River Endrick from this area. The sewage from this town would almost certainly have to pass into the River Endrick, and any effluent of such a volume must greatly increase the pollution risk in a river which is, after all, only of a relatively small size. It would be particularly harmful if this effluent were to be passed into the Blane Water, for, as described above, this already receives the effluents from three separate communities. It would seem that the present scheme for this town (which has met with many objections from parties interested in the area) has, for the moment at least, been shelved; but if it is suggested again much consideration must be given to the effect which it will certainly have on the River Endrick and its fauna. Even more recently than the above scheme, a tentative proposal has been put forward to start a building development comprising some 2500 houses in that part of the Endrick valley just south of Blanefield (Fig. 18). Clearly such a scheme will present similar difficulties to the one at Finnich which has just been discussed, with consequent results on the river and its fauna.

IX. The Biology of the Main River

Physical and Chemical Features

Undoubtedly, many of the reasons for the restriction of any species to a particular environment lie in the basic chemical and physical features pertaining to that environment. Difficulty of collection and transportation—especially in the upper reaches—made it impossible to carry out regular observations at many stations on the River Endrick, and only three stations were examined in detail. These have been described above in the section dealing with quantitative studies. At all twelve stations on the main river (Fig. 20), only certain chemical and physical data were obtained; these are considered below, together with information available from map analysis and other sources.

Current

In general, the average current speed of any particular stretch of the river is a function of the gradient of the river bed in that stretch. Many local factors may alter this theoretical speed, whilst, of course, the current in any one part of the river varies from the edge to the middle and from the substrate to the water surface; nevertheless, gradient is the main controlling factor. Fig. 20 is a profile of the main River Endrick from mouth to source: it can be seen that in the upper reaches for some distance below the source the gradient is steep. In the middle reaches, the gradient becomes much less severe, whilst in the lower reaches it is very slight indeed, especially near the river mouth. This variation in gradient agrees with the general description of the River Endrick given above, where it was pointed out that in much of the upper reaches the current is fast and turbulent, in the middle reaches it is fast but turbulent only in stretches of riffle, and in the lower reaches it is slow with very little turbulence. It should be noted that the change from source to mouth is for the most part a gradual one.

A profile of this type is characteristic of a fairly mature river (Green and Moon, 1936). Irregularities unique to the River Endrick, which affect the local current greatly, are few but nevertheless of

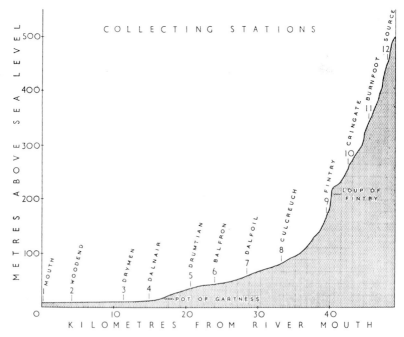

Fig. 20.—A profile of the River Endrick, showing the main collecting stations and the two major waterfalls on the main river

great importance to the biology of some parts of the river. As mentioned above, there are two waterfalls of importance; the Pot of Gartness, which is some 3 m. high (see Plate 6 in Stuart, 1962), and the Loup of Fintry, which is about 30 m. high (Plate VB). These affect the general profile of the river but little, and there is no evidence that they influence the distribution of any of the common species of invertebrate found there. They do have an important effect on the distribution of certain species of fish, however, because of the inability of these fish to surmount them and reach the stretches of river above.

The presence of Loch Lomond, into which the River Endrick flows (Fig. 1), has an important influence on the flow and water level in the lower reaches; because of the slight gradient here the damming effect of water in the loch influences the river for some considerable distance upstream, and may result in differences between the variations in water level in the lower and the middle reaches (Fig. 7). Whilst the water level and flow in the middle and upper reaches depend on the rainfall in these parts of the Endrick valley, the water level and flow in the lower reaches depend both on the rainfall in the Endrick valley and on that in other parts of the Loch Lomond watershed. Much of the latter district has a higher average annual rainfall than the Endrick area.

It is convenient at this point to note that one of the most characteristic and obvious features about the flow of water in a river, compared with, say, that of a wave-washed lake shore, is that it is completely unidirectional, flowing constantly from source to mouth. Movement of animals in a downstream direction presents few problems, and any species which becomes established in one particular part of the river should have little difficulty in spreading downstream and populating suitable habitats there. It is now a well-established fact that many rivers possess a marked organic drift (Müller, 1954), in which members of the bottom fauna at times play a prominent part; many invertebrates must be distributed in this manner in such river systems. Movement in the reverse direction is much more difficult, the ability of any aquatic species to move upstream depending mainly on its powers of negotiating the current— particularly at waterfalls—in the river above. Many river species show a positive rheotaxy (Carpenter, 1928) and this is present not only in the aquatic stages, but also in the terrestrial adults of several species. Roos (1957) has clearly demonstrated that the adult females of several species of Trichoptera always fly upstream before ovipositing.

Substrate

It has previously been noted that the condition of the substrate at any point in the river is very largely dependent on the nature and speed of the current there, but that, in spite of its being a secondary characteristic, the substrate type is often a much more convenient way of referring to each habitat, because of the difficulties of current measurement (Percival and Whitehead, 1929). The general nature of the substrate in the River Endrick has also been described above, it being sufficient to note here that there is a basic succession from source to mouth—this being peat, rock, boulder, stone, gravel, sand and silt. These are not differentiated sharply one from the other, but merge gradually from source to mouth, with occasional irregularities (e.g. where bare rock is exposed in the lower reaches of the river). Because of the slower nature of the current at the edge of the river in any stretch, there is a distinct tendency for this part of the bed to be more silted than that in midstream. (See also Macan, 1961*b*.)

Temperature

It is established that in any given latitude the average temperature tends to decrease with altitude; Halstead (1958) has pointed out the importance of this effect in the hilly areas round Glasgow. Its importance in relation to aquatic habitats depends on many factors, notably the size of the water body concerned, the origin of its water supply (surface or underground), and its degree of exposure. The basic difference in flow between lakes and rivers means that these must be considered separately with reference to altitude; and here only rivers will be discussed.

The direct effect of altitude on the River Endrick means that the higher parts of the river will tend to be cooler than the lower: thus the average temperature of the river might be expected to increase from source to mouth. Carpenter (1928) has stated that as a stream passes from source to mouth its temperature "changes in closer accordance with that of the air, owing to the larger exposure to its influence and to the widening of the valley". The temperature data for the streams studied by Illies (1952) and Dittmar (1955) agree with this statement—the average annual temperature range increasing in a downstream direction—and it is probably true of most small streams. The situation with larger streams and rivers, however, is not necessarily the same, the temperature data obtained in the River Endrick (Fig. 8), for instance, showing that the situation there is quite different. It might, indeed, be expected that, in many cases, on theoretical grounds alone, the statement of Carpenter (1928) would not always be valid. The volume of water in most rivers increases from source to mouth at a rate which depends on the number and sizes of the tributaries which it receives (see below); since a small body of water will change in temperature more quickly than a larger one in relation to its surroundings, it is clear that the temperature range in the upper river could well be more extreme than that further downstream. The river water in the upper reaches, moreover, is shallow and turbulent, and there is much more contact with the atmosphere here than in the lower reaches, where the water is deep and there is little turbulence. This, too, means that the temperature of the water in the upper river will follow that of the air much more quickly than that in the lower river, and a study of the weekly variations in temperature during 1960 (Fig. 8) at station A (Woodend) in the lower reaches, and station B (Drumtian) in the middle reaches, shows that this is in fact the case in these parts of the River Endrick.

Thus in the upper river, whilst altitude means a lower average temperature, the small size of the river and its turbulence mean that the temperature will follow that of the atmosphere rapidly: the opposite is the case in the lower river. A third factor complicates the issue, however, this being concerned with whether the bulk of water supplying the river is of surface or underground origin. Whilst surface water might normally be expected to have a similar temperature to that of the air (though this is evidently not always the case, for Hynes (1961) has shown that the upper waters of the Afon Hirnant are consistently cooler in summer and warmer in winter than the lower waters—even though the stream is not spring fed), underground water from springs is usually of a very constant low temperature, and this may affect the temperature regime considerably, offsetting as it does the effect of small size and turbulence.

In the River Endrick almost all parts reach 0°C. during most winters. The rate of change in temperature is more extreme in the middle river than in the lower, though the average temperature of the river water increases from source to mouth. Maximum temperatures in the lower reaches are rarely above 20°C.; in the middle reaches—where the river is considerably smaller but the altitude only slightly greater—maximum temperatures are a degree or so higher; whilst in the upper reaches the high altitude means that the water temperatures rarely goes above 16°C.

Volume

The importance of the size of a river at any point has already been stressed in connection with temperature variation; it also has a bearing on several other important factors. The general conception of a river is of one which starts as a small trickle at its source and increases in size very gradually all the way to its mouth. The actual situation is often far from this ideal, for the nature of the average volume of water carried by a river at any point depends on the character of the watershed involved. Gradual volume increases are typical of rivers which have long narrow watersheds, e.g. the River Teifi (Jones, 1943). River watersheds, however, are often of shapes other than this, and the main river, instead of receiving its water from many small tributaries, is supplied by fewer tributaries which may vary greatly in size. In such cases the volume change from source to mouth will not be a gradual one, but will tend to have a "stepped" appearance.

An estimate of the change in volume of the water at various points along the River Endrick from source to mouth is given in Fig. 21, based on data available for the watershed areas at these points. Though such a method is rather a crude one, it does seem to be the best available in the absence of reliable gauging records from the river itself. In general, it can be seen that the increase from source to mouth is for the most part a gradual one, for much of the water is received from small tributaries which enter frequently (cf. Fig. 1). The only exception to this is where the inflow from the Blane Water is received: this is by far the largest tributary entering the main river, having a total watershed area of 6,734 hectares. (The watershed area of the main river above their junction is 11,396 hectares, whilst that of the whole river system is 26,677 hectares.) The influence of the Blane Water on the main river could, therefore, be an important one, not only in connection with temperature stability, but also with other factors—such as chemical composition, etc.—and the distribution of certain invertebrate species shows that this is in fact the case.

Composition of the river water

Detailed information concerning the composition of the river water at station A (Woodend) and station B (Drumtian) on the River Endrick has been given in Table 5. In Table 21 the averages of eight

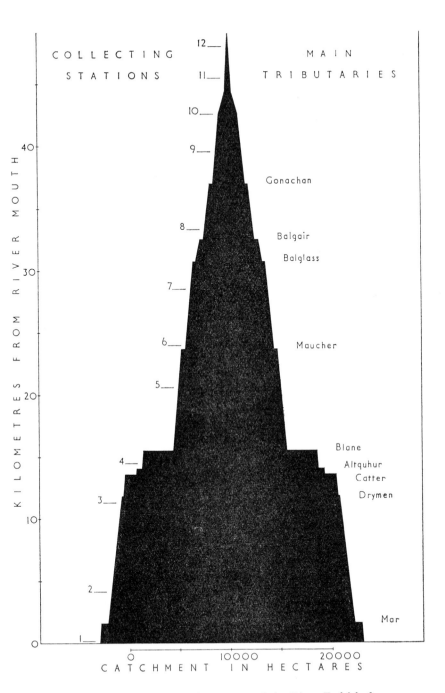

Fig. 21.—The changes in catchment area of the River Endrick from source to mouth

167

Table 21.—Average chemical analyses (in milligrams per litre) of eight series of water samples taken from ten stations (*a* to *j*) on the River Endrick between 4th May, 1961 and 19th September, 1963

	(a)	(b)	(c)	(d)	(e)	(f)	(g)	(h)	(i)	(j)
Kilos. from river mouth	4·8	10·8	15·9	18·9	22·1	23·5	28·8	34·1	36·2	40·2
Ave. Temp. (°C)	10·4	9·9	10·0	10·9	10·0	9·6	9·8	9·3	9·3	9·5
pH	7·4	7·5	7·6	7·5	7·4	7·4	7·5	7·1	7·1	7·0
Suspended Solids	8	15	13	10	7	7	7	5	4	5
Chloride (as Cl)	11	11	9	9	9	8	7	7	7	7
Alkalinity (as CaCO$_3$)	57	56	53	49	50	44	39	29	27	16
Ammoniacal Nitrogen	0·27	0·25	0·19	0·21	0·19	0·13	0·20	0·16	0·14	0·24
Albuminoid Nitrogen	0·17	0·17	0·18	0·16	0·20	0·18	0·16	0·13	0·16	0·15
Nitrous Nitrogen	0·01	0·01	trace	trace	trace	trace	trace	trace	nil	nil
Nitric Nitrogen	0·44	0·37	0·31	0·32	0·32	0·31	0·17	0·14	0·21	0·07
Dissolved Oxygen	10·8	11·2	11·7	11·8	11·6	11·7	11·8	11·6	11·6	11·5
% Sat. Diss. Oxygen	99·1	101·3	106·5	107·9	105·6	105·4	106·5	104·0	103·7	102·8
B.O.D.	1·6	2·0	1·9	2·1	1·9	2·1	1·5	1·2	1·5	1·4

series of analyses of water taken at ten stations on the main river at different times of the year by the Clyde River Purification Board are given. One might expect the river water, starting off as it does in bare moorland, to be rather poor in dissolved salts at first, but to increase the concentration of these as it passes downstream to the mouth; such data as are available show that this is for the most part true. The main factors bringing about this increase are undoubtedly the underlying rocks of the valley (Fig. 1) and the changes brought about by man (Maitland, 1962b).

It is recognized that two of the most useful indicators of the "richness" of a water body are its calcium content and its pH value; several workers have shown these to be of great importance in the distribution of various groups of animals (Macan, 1950; Mann, 1955; and Reynoldson, 1958). Samples of river water, taken at eleven stations on the main river as close together in time as was possible, were analyzed for these two factors on two separate occasions—one when the river was high, the other when the river was low. The average results are given in Fig. 22A, from which it can be seen that

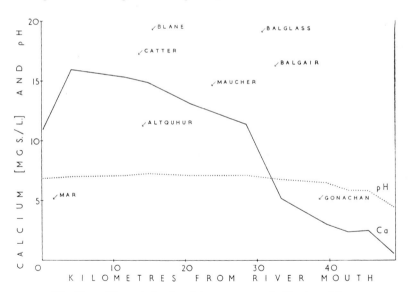

Fig. 22A.—The variation in calcium content and pH value of the water from source to mouth in the River Endrick. The calcium content and point of entry of each of the main tributaries is also indicated in this figure

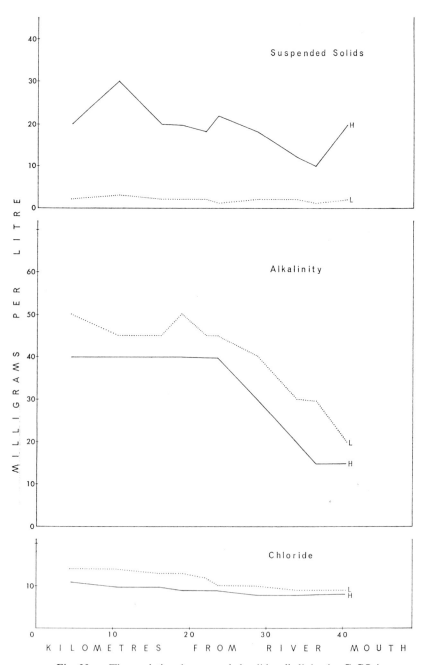

Fig. 22B.—The variation in suspended solids, alkalinity (as CaCO₃)
and chloride (as Cl) present in the water of the River Endrick on
(*a*) 4th May, 1961 (L). (*b*) 13th March, 1963 (H)

the calcium content and pH value of the river water increase from the source to near the mouth, much of this increase taking place as the river receives water from tributaries flowing over areas of calciferous sandstone (Fig. 1). The reason for the lowered calcium values at the mouth of the river is possibly the influence of water from Loch Lomond. The station sampled here (station 1, Mouth) is only 200 m. from the outflow of the River Endrick into Loch Lomond—the water of the loch having a lower calcium content (about 10·4 mg./l. in the lower loch) than much of the river (Slack, 1957*b*)—and there is some evidence that on occasions mixing may take place actually above the river mouth. Fig. 22A shows also that the calcium contents of the main tributaries may vary considerably, and presumably each influences the main river in proportion to its relative size at their junction (Fig. 21).

The amount of suspended matter carried by the river water varies from source to mouth (Fig. 22B). General observations show that though the water in the upper reaches of the river is more coloured than that further downstream (due to the influence of peat) it contains relatively little in the way of suspended matter, except during spates. In passing downstream the turbidity of the water increases, and part of this is due to the influence of sewage effluents which enter the river in its middle and lower reaches (Maitland, 1962*b*). At station B (Drumtian) in the middle reaches, the water carries an average of 7 mg./l. suspended solids; and at station A (Woodend) in the lower reaches, about 9 mg./l.

Biological Features

One of the main purposes of the present study was to find out how animals and higher plants are distributed in the main part of the River Endrick. Macan (1961*a*) has pointed out that in the past, because of the difficulties involved in the identification of many aquatic animals, it has been impossible to discuss adequately the characteristic typology of rivers on a fundamental (i.e. species) level. In the present account it has been in large part possible to overcome this factor—mainly because of the many useful keys published in recent years for the identification of British aquatic animals, and also because of the help given to the author by the many specialists acknowledged elsewhere. Among the larger invertebrates, only some families of Trichoptera and most Diptera (other than Simuliidae) prevent the analysis from being a comprehensive one. Also, as Hynes (1961) has pointed out, the aquatic fauna of Great Britain is much less rich than that of the rest of Europe, and this simplifies the task of community analysis in studies undertaken in this country.

No attempt was made to examine the microflora of the River Endrick, and as a result very little is known about their distribution. The important species of macroflora occurring in the river have already been discussed (Fig. 3) and the presence of most of them is apparently correlated with local conditions of current and substrate. Whilst all the species present in the river are clearly restricted to certain stretches, there is no single scheme of zonation which is applicable to them all, there being a transition of species associations from mouth to source.

The occurrence of those species of fish found in the River Endrick has also been discussed above (Fig. 11) and it was pointed out that the distribution of many of them is restricted by certain unusual local conditions, i.e. the two high waterfalls which occur on the main river. The lower of these—the Pot of Gartness—is the one of least importance; both Salmon and Trout can negotiate it at certain water levels (Stuart, 1962), and though it does prevent both Perch and Roach from reaching the river above it is unlikely that either of these species would find the conditions further upstream suitable for them to become established there. The Loup of Fintry (Plate VB) is a barrier which prevents all fish from passing upstream, and, though five species are common in the river just below, only one of these (Brown Trout) is common above the fall. Other than at these two points there is no clear evidence for zonation among the fish species considered as a whole, a transition of associations being again apparent. The abrupt division of communities by waterfalls, though of interest in itself, is clearly a local phenomenon, and of little relevance when discussing the general implications of zonation in rivers.

The evaluation of significant species

The degree to which different species of invertebrates exhibit zonation varies considerably, some being common in many parts of the river, others only in certain restricted stretches. Having now examined the main physical and chemical characteristics of the River Endrick from source to mouth, it is possible to consider how the distribution of various species of invertebrates can be related to them. The material on which this distribution analysis is based is the series of timed collections (described fully above) which were taken at twelve stations along the main river from source to mouth, supplemented by other collections taken occasionally at other points. Macan (1957*b*) has pointed out that timed handnet collections of this type are one of the few feasible ways of comparing the fauna of different habitats in a stream. In the present account, in order to afford some measure of comparison between different stations, the number of each species collected in one hour at each station has been calculated. Essentially, this represents the total number of each species taken in ten-minute collections from the two main habitats at each station at the three times of sampling—February, June and October. This rough basis of comparison is a useful one, for whilst the main feature in the distribution of any species is its presence or absence at a station, it is also important to have some idea of its relative abundance there (see also Fig. 4).

Each species must fulfil certain requirements before being considered of value in any assessment of zonation: firstly it must be possible to identify it accurately to species level—this excludes the very young individuals of many groups and all the larvae of Diptera (except Simuliidae and a few minor families) and the larvae of some families of Trichoptera and Coleoptera. It is especially unfortunate that at present most larval Chironomidae can be identified no further than the genus, for this family is always an important part of the bottom fauna, and several different forms show a restricted distribution. Secondly, before it can be of value in any classification of distribution, each species must be present in certain abundance. In the present study, only those animals of which more than five specimens were collected per hour (see above) at any one station are regarded as being significant; each species so selected was considered to be present regularly at any station below that of maximum occurrence if two or more specimens were collected there per hour, and above the station of maximum occurrence if even one or more was collected there per hour (cf. Berg, 1948).

The only exceptions to the above conditions which are included in the present analysis, are a few species which did not occur regularly in the normal collections, but for which special collections were made at each station: these include *Velia caprai*, *Gerris lacustris* and *Anodonta anatina*. A few species which did qualify for inclusion are not considered because of their special dependence on some other invertebrate, e.g. *Chaetogaster limnaei*, a commensal species found in the mantle cavity of several species of gastropod.

Well over one hundred different species of invertebrate qualify for consideration under the above scheme: to obtain as clear a picture as possible of their distribution they have been divided into two arbitrary classes—(a) Those with a widespread distribution, which occurred at more than half the stations examined (Fig. 23A). (b) Those with a limited distribution, which were found at only half or fewer of the stations examined (Fig. 23B). It can be seen from these two figures that animals with all types of range occur, from those species which are extremely restricted, e.g. *Ameletus inopinatus*, to those which are found in all parts of the river, e.g. *Limnius tuberculatus*. Only a few of the latter type are present, however, for the distribution of the great majority of invertebrate species in the River Endrick appears to be restricted in some way.

Transition of species associations

Approximately one-third of the species under consideration have a widespread distribution (Fig. 23A); all of these occur in the middle reaches of the river, and adequate collections taken at places between 20 and 30 km. from the mouth should reveal them there. As has just been mentioned, even these species are mostly restricted in some way, those which are present in the lower reaches tending to be absent in the upper reaches, and vice versa. Most of these animals therefore exhibit zonation as species, but few of them do so collectively (Fig. 23A), there being a complete transition in the associations of

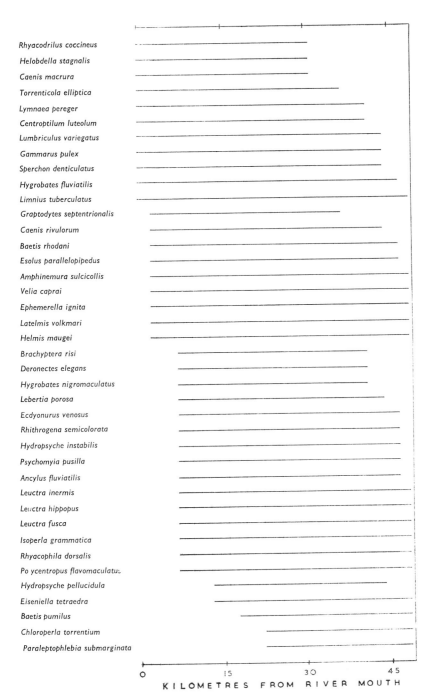

Rhyacodrilus coccineus
Helobdella stagnalis
Caenis macrura
Torrenticola elliptica
Lymnaea pereger
Centroptilum luteolum
Lumbriculus variegatus
Gammarus pulex
Sperchon denticulatus
Hygrobates fluviatilis
Limnius tuberculatus
Graptodytes septentrionalis
Caenis rivulorum
Baetis rhodani
Esolus parallelopipedus
Amphinemura sulcicollis
Velia caprai
Ephemerella ignita
Latelmis volkmari
Helmis maugei
Brachyptera risi
Deronectes elegans
Hygrobates nigromaculatus
Lebertia porosa
Ecdyonurus venosus
Rhithrogena semicolorata
Hydropsyche instabilis
Psychomyia pusilla
Ancylus fluviatilis
Leuctra inermis
Leuctra hippopus
Leuctra fusca
Isoperla grammatica
Rhyacophila dorsalis
Po ycentropus flavomaculatu
Hydropsyche pellucidula
Eiseniella tetraedra
Baetis pumilus
Chloroperla torrentium
Paraleptophlebia submarginata

O   I 5   3 0   4 5

KILOMETRES FROM RIVER MOUTH

Fig. 23A.—The distribution of widespread invertebrate species in the
River Endrick

species present from source to mouth. There is thus little evidence for distinct zonation in the River Endrick with these widespread forms, other than at species level.

The remaining two-thirds of the species being considered are much more restricted in their distribution, and Fig. 23B shows that many of them are confined to stretches of 15 km. or less in the river. The zonation of each of them, therefore, is clear; as with the more widespread species, however, it can be seen that there is little evidence of distinct zonation from source to mouth when these restricted forms are considered collectively, a transition of species being once again apparent.

By the judicious selection of certain species, it would be possible to draw up several schemes of zonation within the River Endrick, but no one scheme would be true for all the species associations found there. Several groups of species show a definite restriction of distribution at generic, family, and occasionally even ordinal level, and could be used in a scheme of zonation at these levels. Great caution would be necessary in applying such a scheme, however, for it could well be inapplicable in different rivers, where other species are present—no matter how closely related they might be.

The data in Figs. 23A and 23B show that Hemiptera are completely restricted to the lower reaches of the River Endrick, with the exception of *Velia caprai*—this species is common in all parts of the river, thus nullifying the zonation of the rest of the order and giving it a widespread distribution from source to mouth. The situation is somewhat similar with Mollusca, which are also restricted to the lower reaches of the river, with the exception of *Lymnaea pereger* and *Ancylus fluviatilis* (Fig. 23A). The latter species in particular can be found high in the upper reaches—though not at the source—it and a closely related species affording a supreme example of how mistaken impressions regarding zonation can be formed, if animals are considered above species level. Ancylidae occur in most parts of the river from the mouth to within a short distance of the source, the family thus showing little evidence of zonation. At species level, however, a distinct zonation is evident—*Acroloxus lacustris* being common in the extreme lower reaches, where *Ancylus fluviatilis* is absent, the reverse being the case in the middle and upper reaches.

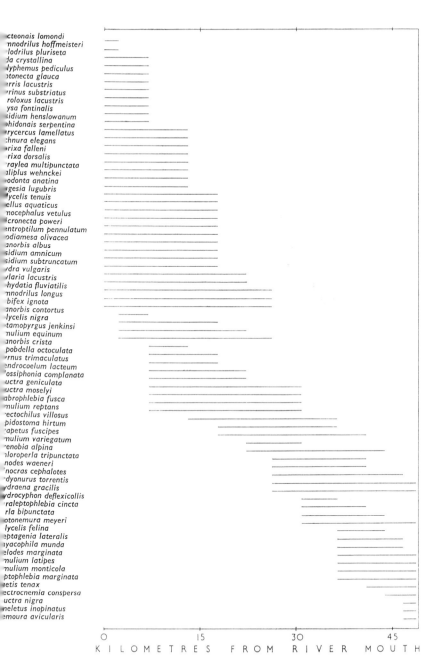

Fig. 23B.—The distribution of local invertebrate species in the River
Endrick

177

The statement by Macan (1961*a*) that "the species is the basic unit in ecology" is clearly a valid one when dealing with the zonation of rivers, and the use of groupings higher than species tends to be unreliable. When the distribution of each species is examined in relation to its abundance at each station a general pattern emerges: each is usually common in one part of the river only and each decreases in abundance both upstream and downstream until it is absent. The critical threshold of any limiting factor or factors is presumably reached at such points, and the diminution in number to this point from the maximum is normally a gradual one—not a sudden reduction as should be expected if true zonation occurred.

It has been pointed out above that certain species in the River Endrick do exhibit an abrupt distribution—being common at one place in the river but absent a few metres upstream. Obvious examples of this are Salmon, Minnow and Stone Loach which are common below the Loup of Fintry but absent or rare above it; this is true zonation and the reason for it is clear. Among the invertebrates, too, distinct distributions occur, notable among which is the distribution of three unrelated species—*Erpobdella octoculata*, *Asellus aquaticus* and *Potamopyrgus jenkinsi*. These are all common in the main river below its junction with the Blane Water, but are absent or certainly very uncommon in all stretches above this point. The macrophytes *Potamogeton crispus* and *Elodea canadensis* have a similar distribution; the reason for this sharp zonation is not yet certain, but is probably connected with the more polluted nature of the Blane Water compared with the main river (Maitland, 1962*b*). Though the distribution of these five species stops sharply in the main river at its junction with the Blane Water, all of them are common in the latter stream for several kilometres above this point.

Other even more extreme examples of restricted distribution are of course found in the vicinity of sewage effluents; these have been discussed elsewhere (Maitland, 1962*b*). In all these cases—the only ones where true zonation has been shown to occur—the factors responsible will vary greatly from river to river, having, therefore, little relevance in any discussion on the zonation of rivers in general.

Zonation

Several workers have devised schemes of zonation for rivers which they have studied; most of them have restricted themselves to one group of animals or plants. Carpenter (1928), adapting the earlier schemes of continental workers (e.g. Thienemann, 1912, and Steinmann, 1915) to British rivers, based her various zones on the distribution of common fish species. Whilst such a scheme could be true for the few species concerned it is not necessarily true for other animals and plants; in addition, fish are easily affected by barriers in the river, natural or otherwise, their distribution varying accordingly. Huet (1946) also suggests that fish zones are evident in rivers, and Schmitz (1955) has claimed that invertebrate biocenoses corresponding to these zones can be recognized. Macan (1961*a*) points out that this is not the case; fish are mobile and can range over what might really be several types of invertebrate habitat.

Tansley (1939) classified rivers into five zones on the basis of the vegetation present; but, as with many other accounts of zonation in rivers, what he really describes as zones are in fact certain definite stretches along a river, the areas between them being transitional and some species occurring in several '"zones". The distribution of vegetation in a river, as was mentioned earlier, is in large part correlated with the different substrates found there. On such physical features Harrison and Elsworth (1958) based their initial scheme of zonation for the Great Berg River, claiming that the fauna and flora followed a similar pattern. It is evident, however, from their subsequent and very valuable account of this river, that, as in the River Endrick, the basic feature in the distribution of species associations there is one of transition and not true zonation. In the Tugela River Oliff (1960) recognizes eight "distinct" zones, basing them on gradient and associated fauna; his results showing, however, that here too transitions and not distinct zonation are found.

Marlier (1951), in trying to analyze animal associations, notes that only small ones can be recognized (which he characterizes by the dominant species of invertebrate present), suggesting that synecological studies will be the important ones of the future. Macan (1961*a*) points out that this will lead to very complex schemes and thus defeat

13   SLL

the end of any scheme of classification, which is to marshal ideas on a simple plan from which further advance can be made. In this paper and an earlier one (1957*b*) he suggests that in a general way river systems can be zoned according to the Ephemeroptera present, but in the evidence put forward to support this contention once again transitions are apparent. Given sets of species do form distinct zones, but others overlap these zones, they themselves being restricted at other points. Macan (1961*a*) himself points out that the important question is whether or not the divisions chosen for the zonation of each group fall at the same points, and notes that, though many more data are necessary, such as are available at present suggest that this is not so.

The different populations of invertebrates found in the Fulda River by Illies (1953) were examined by counting the total number of species which occurred at any one station and also how many of these were found at other stations upstream and downstream. Illies maintains that if such data are plotted as a graph it will be evident where each biocenosis ends and where each starts. A similar procedure has been carried out for the common species occurring at twelve stations in the River Endrick, the results being given in Fig. 24. From this graph several conclusions can be reached. There is a distinct difference between the communities found at stations 1 and 2 and those found at stations 5 to 12, these communities being in fact the basic ones of the lentic and lotic associations discussed by Carpenter (1928). Stations 3 and 4, however, form a transition between these communities; this is almost certainly the reason for the larger number of species occurring there. Between station 5 and station 12, as one moves upstream, there is a very gradual transition from one association to another.

It would seem from this examination, therefore, that any scheme of zonation applied to the River Endrick could be only an arbitrary one, which might be true for some plants or animals, but would not be true for others and thus not true for the river as a whole. This justifies the statement of Schwoerbel (1961) that "the very wide variety of animals and conditions found in rivers suggests that no scheme of zonation will ever be found". The transitions described above are, in fact, the result of this large number of variable factors

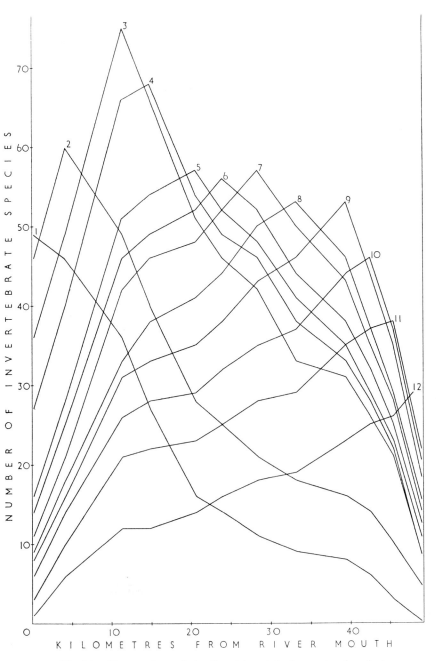

Fig. 24.—The numbers of significant invertebrate species found at each station in the River Endrick (Fig. 2), plotted with the numbers of the same species which are present at other stations upstream and downstream

181

operating on the distribution of different species in the River Endrick. Some species are limited by temperature, others by substrate, amount of suspended matter, calcium, etc. Not only are these factors usually transitional in themselves from the extremes normally found at source and mouth, but if by chance there is a sharp change in one of them (e.g. a sudden increase in calcium where a highly calcareous tributary enters the main river) there would rarely be a change in any of the others at the same point. Thus the general theme of the change in biotic associations from source to mouth in a river will tend to be one not of zonation but of transition.

Running Water Classification

The attempts to classify running waters have in the past been of two kinds: firstly the division of different parts of a river system into definable zones, and secondly the separation of different river systems into definable types. The first of these has already been discussed, and only the relationship between different river systems will be considered further in the present account.

The classification of Ontario streams devised by Ricker (1934) divides rivers into primary groups on the basis of the volume of water flowing on 1st June of each year, into secondary groups on the basis of temperature, current speed and type of substrate, and into tertiary groups on the quantity of dissolved solids present. This scheme has been criticized by several workers (e.g. Berg, 1948; Badcock, 1953b) mostly because of the fact that it is too arbitrary—this being especially true of the primary divisions. It is clear too—and this is true of many schemes of river classification—that any river system might well fit into several different categories under this scheme, depending on where the data were collected in that river. Carpenter (1927) classified certain streams according to their origin, and Butcher (1933) also used the type of origin for a primary classification, further division being dependent on the type of substrate present and whether or not the water was acid or alkaline.

Moon (1938) has suggested that in classifications of streams (and lake shores) the erosion and deposition of silt are important factors. Hynes (1941), however, points out that this may be satisfactory for major divisions but does not lead to any obvious method on which a detailed classification could be made. Hynes then classifies stonefly habitats in running water initially on their size and the type of substrate present, then on their altitude and the stability of the substrate. Obviously many such different habitats could all be found within a single river system. Macan (1961*a*) points out that river systems can be divided into general types according to the species of Ephemeroptera present in them; this method would not, however, take into account regional differences, which Illies (1955) has shown to be considerable, even in Europe.

The classification of streams according to the average density and weight of bottom fauna present in a standard area has been proposed on several occasions, mostly by American workers (e.g. Lagler, 1949). The latter designated streams as rich if the number of organisms in a square metre was more than 500, and their weight more than 21 grams; as average if the number was more than 500 and their weight between 11 and 21 grams per square metre; and as poor if the number of animals in each square metre was fewer than 500 and their weight less than 11 grams. Such schemes are not only very arbitrary but they are also very impracticable, and Badcock (1953*b*) suggests that they are of doubtful value. A large amount of labour is necessary to establish the required figures (which vary from month to month), and the correlation between numbers of animals and their weights is not always a straightforward one, as the quantitative studies discussed above have shown. A further criticism is that such schemes rarely make suggestions as to where in each river the samples should be taken; it has been shown that in the River Endrick there are considerable differences between the numbers and weights of animals found in different substrates, and that even the same substrate may be more productive in one part of the river than in another.

One of the most valuable discussions on the classification of running waters is that of Berg (1948): he points out that rivers cannot be classified like lakes because they are not uniform entities, but are systems which change from source to mouth. It is not therefore possible to undertake ecological groupings of rivers, but merely of certain reaches within them, and the unit in such a system will not be an entire water course, but a stretch of one within which the environment is in the main uniform—i.e. a biotope. The problem of classifying running waters is thus one of describing these biotopes and their faunas, and Berg notes that there is still a great dearth of information about these, for the fauna of few rivers has been studied in detail.

In the discussion of zonation in the River Endrick, it was pointed out that the distribution of the species associations in the main river is not clear-cut but is transitional. It is, however, possible to analyze the fauna and conditions in any one stretch, and the main biotopes found in the river have already been described and classified. Such a step seems basic to any critical evaluation of a river system, for only then is it possible to compare the differences within the river itself and contrast these with other rivers or parts of rivers which have been described by other workers.

Diagnosis of the River Endrick

In his study of Loch Lomond, Weerekoon (1956) refrained from placing it in any of the accepted lake-classification systems, giving merely a brief description of its most salient features. The position with river classification is even more complex than that with lakes, and the present author too feels that a specific and accurate diagnosis of the main characteristics of the River Endrick will be of far greater value than an elaborate and arbitrary attempt to classify it. Accordingly, the present account of the fauna of the river will be terminated by such a description.

In the upper reaches of the River Endrick the main substrate is peat near the source followed by bare rock and boulders further downstream. The river here is small and the gradient is steep (about 1 in 25). Much of the river flows at heights of over 300 m. and the dissolved salt content of the water is poor (calcium being about 2 mg./l.). Macrophytic flora consists only of mosses and the invertebrate fauna is poor in the total number of species present—though several of these are characteristic of this stretch, e.g. *Ameletus inopinatus*, *Leuctra nigra* and *Plectrocnemia conspersa*. Trout is the only species of fish to occur here. Other common invertebrate species in the upper reaches are *Ecdyonurus torrentis*, *Baetis pumilus*, *Pro-*

tonemura meyeri, Chloroperla torrentium, Dinocras cephalotes and *Hydraena gracilis.* These occur also further downstream, in the middle reaches of the river, where the main substrate gradually changes from boulders to stones, and thereafter from stones to gravel. The river in these middle reaches is now larger but the gradient is much less steep (about 1 in 100) than further upstream. Much of it flows at altitudes of under 150 metres, and the dissolved salt content of the water is moderate (calcium being about 8 mg./l.). The dominant macrophyte here is *Fontinalis antipyretica* but *Myriophyllum alterniflorum* also occurs, whilst the invertebrate fauna is rich with regard to the total number of species found, only a few of these, however, being characteristic—e.g. *Chloroperla tripunctata, Tinodes waeneri* and *Simulium variegatum.* No fish are restricted to this part of the river, but Salmon, Trout, Minnows, Stone Loach and Three-spined Sticklebacks all occur both here and further downstream in the lower reaches; as do several invertebrates—*Helobdella stagnalis, Leuctra geniculata, Leuctra moselyi, Simulium reptans* and *Orectochilus villosus.* In the lower reaches the substrate of coarse gravel gives way to sand and eventually to fine silt near the mouth. Here the river is large and the gradient slight (about 1 in 3000) whilst the dissolved salt content is relatively high (calcium being about 15 mg./l.), and the entire river flows at altitudes less than 20 m. The number of species, both of plants and animals, which occur here is high, and many of them are characteristic—e.g. *Potamogeton natans, Potamogeton crispus, Nuphar lutea, Polycelis nigra, Polycelis tenuis, Nymphula nymphaeata* and many species of Oligochaeta, Hirudinea, Hemiptera and Mollusca which do not occur further upstream. Pike, Perch and Roach are characteristic fish of this part of the river.

The total number of animal species occurring in the River Endrick is probably about 300. In the middle reaches, the invertebrate fauna of the dominant substrate (stones) has an average standing crop of some 16 g./m², whilst an equivalent figure for the dominant substrate of the lower reaches (sand) is about 8 g./m². These figures compare favourably with several of those available for other rivers which have been studied in the world to date.

REFERENCES

Albrecht, M. L., 1953. "Die Plane und andere Flämingbäche." *Z. Fisch. (N.F.)* **1**, 389–476.

Allen, K. R., 1938. "Some observations on the biology of the Trout (*Salmo trutta*) in Windermere." *J. Anim. Ecol.*, **7**, 333–349.

Allen, K. R., 1940. "Studies on the biology of the early stages of the Salmon (*Salmo salar*). 1. Growth in the River Eden." *J. Anim. Ecol.*, **9**, 1–23.

Allen, K. R., 1941. "Studies on the biology of the early stages of the Salmon (*Salmo salar*). 2. Feeding habits." *J. Anim. Ecol.*, **10**, 47–76.

Allen, K. R., 1951. "The Horokiwi Stream. A study of a trout population." *Fish. Bull. Wellington, N.Z.*, **10**, 1–231.

Alm, G., 1919. "Mörrumsåns lax och laxöring." *Medd. K. lantbruksstn. Stockholm*, **216**, 1–141.

Andrewartha, H. G., 1961. *Introduction to the study of animal populations.* London.

Badcock, R. M., 1949. "Studies in stream life in tributaries of the Welsh Dee." *J. Anim. Ecol.*, **18**, 193–208.

Badcock, R. M., 1953a. "Studies of the benthic fauna in tributaries of the Kavlinge River, Southern Sweden." *Rep. Inst. Freshw. Res. Drottning.*, **35**, 21–37.

Badcock, R. M., 1953b. "Comparative studies in the populations of streams." *Rep. Inst. Freshw. Res. Drottning.*, **35**, 38–50.

Bassett, D. A., 1958. *Geological excursion guide to the Glasgow district.* Kendal.

Behning, A., 1924. "Einige Ergebnisse qualitativer und quantitativer Untersuchungen der Bodenfauna der Wolga." *Verh. int. Ver. Limnol.*, **1**, 71–93.

Bennike, S. A. B., 1943. "Contributions to the ecology and biology of the Danish fresh-water leeches (Hirudinea)." *Folia. limnol. scand.*, **2**, 1–109.

Berg, K., 1948. "Biological studies on the River Susaa." *Folia limnol. scand.*, **4**, 1–318.

Berg, K., 1952. "On the oxygen consumption of Ancylidae (Gastropoda) from an ecological point of view." *Hydrobiologia*, **4**, 225–267.

Birch, L. C., 1957. "The meanings of competition." *Amer. Nat.*, **91**, 5–18.

Boycott, A. E., 1936. "The habitats of fresh-water Mollusca in Britain." *J. Anim. Ecol.*, **5**, 116–186.

Brian, M. V., 1956. "Exploitation and interference in interspecies competition." *J. Anim. Ecol.*, **25**, 339–347.

Brinkhurst, R. O., 1959. "The habitats and distribution of British *Gerris* and *Velia* species." *J. Soc. Brit. Ent.*, **6**, 37–44.

Brinkhurst, R. O., 1960. "Introductory studies on the British Tubificidae (Oligochaeta)." *Arch. Hydrobiol. (Plankt.)*, **56**, 395–412.

Brinkhurst, R. O., 1962. "A check-list of British Oligochaeta." *Proc. Zool. Soc. Lond.*, **138**, 317–330.

Brinkhurst, R. O., 1963. "A guide for the identification of British aquatic Oligochaeta." *Sci. Publ. Freshw. Biol. Ass.*, **22**, 1–52.

Brook, A. J., and Woodward, W. B., 1956. "Some observations on the effects of water inflow and outflow on the plankton of small lakes." *J. Anim. Ecol.*, **25**, 22–35.

BROWN, A., 1891. "The fishes of Loch Lomond and its tributaries." *Scot. Nat.*, **10**, 114–124.

BROWN, M. E., 1957. *The physiology of fishes. Volume* 1. *Metabolism.* New York.

BUTCHER, R. W., 1933. "Studies on the ecology of rivers: 1. On the distribution of macrophytic vegetation in the rivers of Britain." *J. Ecol.*, **21**, 58–91.

BUTCHER, R. W., 1959. "Biological assessment of river pollution." *Proc. Linn. Soc. Lond.*, **170**, 159–165.

BUTCHER, R. W., LONGWELL, J., and PENTELOW, F. T. K., 1937. "Survey of the River Tees, III. The non-tidal reaches. Chemical and biological." *Tech. Pap. Wat. Pollut. Res. Lond.*, **6**, 1–187.

BUTCHER, R. W., PENTELOW, F. T. K., and WOODLEY, J. W. A., 1930. "An investigation of the River Lark and the effect of beet sugar pollution." *Fish. Invest., Lond.*, **3**, 1–112.

CARPENTER, K. E., 1927. "Faunistic ecology of some Cardiganshire streams." *J. Ecol.*, **15**, 33–54.

CARPENTER, K. E., 1928. *Life in inland waters.* London.

CARPENTER, K. E., 1940. "The feeding of Salmon parr in the Cheshire Dee." *Proc. Zool. Soc. Lond.*, **110**, 81–96.

CLOUGH, C. T., 1925. *The geology of the Glasgow district.* Edinburgh.

DAY, F., 1880. *The fishes of Great Britain and Ireland.* London.

DENDY, J. S., 1944. "The fate of animals in stream drift when carried into lakes." *Ecol. Monogr.*, **14**, 333–357.

DITTMAR, H., 1955. "Ein Sauerlandbach. Untersuchungen an einem Wiesen-Mittelgebirgsbach." *Arch. Hydrobiol. (Plankt.)*, **50**, 305–552.

EGGLISHAW, H. J., 1964. "The distributional relationship between the bottom fauna and plant detritus in streams." *J. Anim. Ecol.*, **33**, 463–476.

EIDEL, K., 1933. "Beiträge zur Biologie einiger Bache des Schwarzwaldes mit besonderer Berücksichtigung der Insectenfauna der Elz und Kinig." *Arch. Hydrobiol. (Plankt.)*, **25**, 543–615.

ELTON, C., 1946. "Competition and the structure of ecological communities." *J. Anim. Ecol.*, **15**, 54–68.

FRANCK, R., 1658. *Northern memoirs, calculated for the meridian of Scotland.* London.

FROST, W. E., 1939. "River Liffey survey II. The food consumed by the Brown Trout (*Salmo trutta* Linn.) in acid and alkaline waters." *Proc. R. Irish Acad.*, **45**, 139–206.

FROST, W. E., 1942. "River Liffey survey IV. The fauna of the submerged mosses in an acid and an alkaline water." *Proc. R. Irish Acad.*, **47**, 293–369.

FROST, W. E., 1943. "The natural history of the Minnow (*Phoxinus phoxinus*)." *J. Anim. Ecol.*, **12**, 139–162.

FROST, W. E., 1946. "On the food relationships of fish in Windermere." *Biol. Jaarb.*, **13**, 216–231.

FROST, W. E., 1950. "The growth and food of young Salmon (*Salmo salar*) and Trout (*S. trutta*) in the River Forss, Caithness." *J. Anim. Ecol.*, **19**, 147–158.

FROST, W. E., and WENT, A. E. J., 1940. "River Liffey survey III. The growth and food of young Salmon." *Proc. R. Irish Acad.*, **46**, 53–80.

GLEDHILL, T., 1959. "The life-history of *Ameletus inopinatus* (Siphlonuridae, Ephemeroptera)." *Hydrobiologia*, **14**, 85–90.

GREEN, F. H. W., and MOON, H. P., 1936. "The profile of River Avon." *Ann. Rep. Avon Biol. Res.*, **4**, 90–95.

HALSTEAD, C. A., 1958. "The climate of the Glasgow region" in MILLER, R., and TIVY, J., 1958. *The Glasgow Region.* Edinburgh.

HAMILTON, J. D., 1961. "The effect of sand-pit washings on a stream fauna." *Verh. int. Ver. Limnol.*, **14**, 435–439.

HARRISON, A. D., and ELSWORTH, J. F., 1958. "Hydrobiological studies on the Great Berg River, Western Cape Province." *Trans. Roy. Soc. S. Afr.*, **35**, 125–329.

HARTLEY, P. H. T., 1948. "Food and feeding relationships in a community of fresh-water fishes." *J. Anim. Ecol.*, **17**, 1–14.

HESS, A. D., and SWARTZ, A., 1941. "The forage ratio and its use in determining the food grade of streams." *Trans. N.A. Wildlife Conf.*, **5**, 162–164.

HEUTS, M. J., 1946. "De statistische waarde van de methode van Petersen voor het quantitatief onderzoek der bodemfauna." *Biol. Jaarb.* **13**, 200–209.

HOPKINS, C. L., 1962. "Distribution of Hydracarina in the vicinity of Flatford Mill, East Suffolk." *Field Studies*, **1**, 53–72.

HORTON, P. A., 1961. "The bionomics of Brown Trout in a Dartmoor stream." *J. Anim. Ecol.*, **30**, 311–338.

HUET, M., 1946. "Note préliminaire sur les relations entre la pente et les populations piscicoles des eaux courantes." *Biol. Jaarb.*, **13**, 232–243.

HUNTER, L. A., 1960. "Upper Strathendrick." *Unpublished Geography Thesis, University of Glasgow.*

HUNTER, W. R., 1953. "On migrations of *Lymnaea peregra* (Müller) on the shores of Loch Lomond." *Proc. Roy. Soc. Edinb.*, **65**, 84–105.

HUNTER, W. R., 1954. "New and newly-confirmed distribution records of non-marine molluscs in the West of Scotland (IIIrd Paper)." *Glasg. Nat.*, **17**, 207–211.

HUNTER, W. R., 1958. "New and newly-confirmed distribution records of non-marine molluscs in the West of Scotland (IVth Paper)." *Glasg. Nat.*, **18**, 37–44.

HUNTER, W. R., and HAMILTON, J. D., 1958. "*Pisidium* from Hirta, St. Kilda." *J. Conch.*, **24**, 247–248.

HUNTER, W. R., MAITLAND, P. S., and YEOH, P. K. H., 1963. "*Potamopyrgus jenkinsi* in the Loch Lomond area, and an authentic case of passive dispersal." *Proc. Malac. Soc. Lond.*, **36**, 27–32.

HUNTER, W. R., SLACK, H. D., and HUNTER, M., 1959. "The lower vertebrates of the Loch Lomond district." *Glasg. Nat.*, **18**, 84–90.

HYNES, H. B. N., 1941. "The taxonomy and ecology of the nymphs of British Plecoptera with notes on the adults and eggs." *Trans. R. Ent. Soc. Lond.*, **91**, 459–557.

HYNES, H. B. N., 1950. "The food of fresh-water sticklebacks (*Gasterosteus aculeatus* and *Pygosteus pungitius*), with a review of methods used in studies of the food of fishes." *J. Anim. Ecol.*, **19**, 36–58.

HYNES, H. B. N., 1952. "The Plecoptera of the Isle of Man." *Proc. R. Ent. Soc. Lond.*, **27**, 71–76.

HYNES, H. B. N., 1959. "The use of invertebrates as indicators of river pollution." *Proc. Linn. Soc. Lond.*, **170**, 165–169.

HYNES, H. B. N., 1960. *The biology of polluted waters.* Liverpool.

HYNES, H. B. N., 1961. "The invertebrate fauna of a Welsh mountain stream." *Arch. Hydrobiol. (Plankt.)*, **57**, 344–388.

IDE, F. P., 1940. "Quantitative determination of the insect fauna of rapid water." *Univ. Toronto Stud., Biol.*, **47**, 1–20.

IDE, F. P., 1942. "Availability of aquatic insects as food of the Speckled Trout, *Salvelinus fontinalis.*" *Trans. N.A. Wildlife Conf.*, **7**, 442–450.

IDYLL, C. P., 1943. "Bottom fauna of portions of the Cowichan River, B.C." *J. Fish. Res. Bd. Can.*, **6**, 133–139.

ILLIES, J., 1952. "Die Mölle. Faunistisch-ökologische Untersuchungen an einem Forellenbach im Lipper Bergland." *Arch. Hydrobiol. (Plankt.)*, **46**, 424–612.

ILLIES, J., 1953. "Die Besiedlung der Fulda (insbesondere das Benthos der

Salmonidenregion) nach dem jetzigen Stand der Untersuchungen." *Ber. limnol. Flust. Freudenthal*, **5**, 1–28.

ILLIES, J., 1955. "Der biologische Aspekt der limnologischen Flieswassertypisierung." *Arch. Hydrobiol.* (*Plankt.*) *Suppl.*, **22**, 337–346.

JACK, R. L., 1877. "Notes on a till or boulder clay with broken shells, in the lower valley of the River Endrick, near Loch Lomond, and its relation to certain other glacial deposits." *Trans Geol. Soc. Glasg.*, **5**, 5–25.

JONASSON, P. M., 1955. "The efficiency of sieving techniques for sampling freshwater bottom fauna." *Oikos*, **6**, 183–207.

JONES, J. R. E., 1940a. "The fauna of the River Melindwr, a lead-polluted tributary of the River Rheidol in North Cardiganshire, Wales." *J. Anim. Ecol.*, **9**, 188–201.

JONES, J. R. E., 1940b. "A study of the zinc-polluted River Ystwyth in North Cardiganshire, Wales." *Ann. Appl. Biol.*, **27**, 368–378.

JONES, J. R. E., 1941. "The fauna of the River Dovey, West Wales." *J. Anim. Ecol.*, **10**, 12–24.

JONES, J. R. E., 1943. "The fauna of the River Teifi, West Wales." *J. Anim. Ecol.*, **12**, 115–123.

JONES, J. R. E., 1948. "The fauna of four streams in the 'Black Mountain' district of South Wales." *J. Anim. Ecol.*, **17**, 51–65.

JONES, J. R. E., 1949a. "A further ecological study of calcareous streams in the 'Black Mountain' district of South Wales." *J. Anim. Ecol.*, **18**, 142–159.

JONES, J. R. E., 1949b. "An ecological study of the River Rheidol, North Cardiganshire, Wales." *J. Anim. Ecol.*, **18**, 67–88.

JONES, J. R. E., 1950. "A further ecological study of the River Rheidol: the food of the common insects of the main stream." *J. Anim. Ecol.*, **19**, 159–174.

JONES, J. R. E., 1951. "An ecological study of the River Towy." *J. Anim Ecol.*, **20**, 68–86.

JONES, J. R. E., 1958. "A further study of the zinc-polluted River Ystwyth." *J. Anim. Ecol.*, **27**, 1–14.

JONES, J. W., 1959. *The Salmon.* London.

JONES, J. W., and KING, G. M., 1952. "The spawning of the male Salmon parr." *Proc. Zool. Soc. Lond.*, **122**, 615–619.

JONES, N. S., 1952. "The bottom fauna and the food of flatfish off the Cumberland coast." *J. Anim Ecol.*, **21**, 182–205.

KALLEBERG, H., 1958. "Observations in a stream tank of territoriality and competition in juvenile Salmon and Trout (*Salmo salar* L. and *S. trutta* L.)." *Rep. Inst. Freshw. Res. Drottning.*, **39**, 55–98.

KEENLEYSIDE, M. H. A., 1962. "Skin-diving observations of Atlantic Salmon and Brook Trout in the Miramichi River, New Brunswick." *J. Fish. Res. Bd. Can.*, **19**, 625–634.

KIMMINS, D. E., 1944. "Keys to the British species of aquatic Megaloptera and Neuroptera." *Sci. Publ. Freshw. Biol. Ass.*, **8**, 1–20.

KING, J. F. F. X., 1901. "Order Trichoptera" in ELLIOT, G. F. S., LAURIE, M., and MURDOCH, J. B., 1901. *Fauna, flora and geology of the Clyde Area.* Glasgow.

LAGLER, K. F., 1949. *Studies in freshwater fishery biology.* Michigan.

LAMOND, H., 1931. *Loch Lomond.* Glasgow.

LE CREN, E. D., 1958. "Preliminary observations on populations of *Salmo trutta* in becks in Northern England." *Verh. int. Ver. Limnol.*, **13**, 754–757.

LESTAGE, J. A., 1918. "Études sur la biologie des Plécoptères. 1. La larve de *Leuctra geniculata* Stephens." *Ann. Biol. lacust.*, **9**, 257–268.

LINDROTH, A., 1955. "Distribution, territorial behaviour and movements of Sea Trout fry in the River Indalsalven." *Rep. Inst. Freshw. Res. Drottning.*, **36**, 104–119.

LOGAN, S. M., 1963. "Winter observations on bottom organisms and Trout in Bridger Creek, Montana." *Trans. Amer. Fish Soc.*, **92**, 140–145.

LUDWIG, W. B., 1932. "Studies in the animal ecology of the Hocking River basin. The bottom invertebrates of the Hocking River." *Ohio Biol. Surv. Bull.*, **26**, 223–249.

LUMSDEN, J., and BROWN, A., 1895. *A guide to the natural history of Loch Lomond and neighbourhood.* Glasgow.

MACAN, T. T., 1950. "Ecology of fresh-water Mollusca in the English Lake District." *J. Anim. Ecol.*, **19**, 124–146.

MACAN, T. T., 1954. "A contribution to the study of the ecology of Corixidae (Hemipt.)." *J. Anim. Ecol.*, **23**, 115–141.

MACAN, T. T., 1955. "A key to the nymphs of the British species of the family Caenidae (Ephem.)." *Ent. Gaz.*, **6**, 127–142.

MACAN, T. T., 1957*a*. "The life histories and migrations of the Ephemeroptera in a stony stream." *Trans. Soc. Brit. Ent.*, **12**, 129–156.

MACAN, T. T., 1957*b*. "The Ephemeroptera of a stony stream." *J. Anim. Ecol.*, **26**, 317–342.

MACAN, T. T., 1958. "Methods of sampling the bottom fauna in stony streams." *Mitt. int. Ver. Limnol.*, **8**, 1–21.

MACAN, T. T., 1960*a*. "The effect of temperature on *Rhithrogena semicolorata* (Ephem.)." *Int. Rev. ges. Hydrobiol.*, **45**, 197–201.

MACAN, T. T., 1960*b* "The occurrence of *Heptagenia lateralis* (Ephem.) in streams in the English Lake District." *Wett. u. Leben*, **12**, 231–234.

MACAN, T. T., 1961*a*. "A review of running water studies." *Verh. int. Ver. Limnol.*, **14**, 587–602.

MACAN, T. T., 1961*b*. "Factors that limit the range of freshwater animals." *Biol. Rev.*, **36**, 151–198.

MACAN, T. T., 1961*c*. "A key to the nymphs of the British species of Ephemeroptera." *Sci. Publ. Freshw. Biol. Ass.*, **20**, 1–64.

MACAN, T. T., and MACKERETH, J. C., 1957. "Notes on *Gammarus pulex* in the English Lake District." *Hydrobiologia*, **9**, 1–12.

MCCORMACK, J. C., 1962. "The food of young Trout (*Salmo trutta*) in two different becks." *J. Anim. Ecol.*, **31**, 305–316.

MACDONALD, T. H., 1959. "Identification of ammocoetes of British lampreys." *Glasg. Nat.*, **18**, 91–95.

MACKERETH, J. C., 1960. "Notes on the Trichoptera of a stony stream." *Proc. R. Ent. Soc. Lond.*, A, **35**, 17–23.

MCCLEAN, W. N., 1940. "Windermere basin: rainfall, run-off and storage." *Quart. J. R. Met. Soc.*, **66**, 337–362.

MAITLAND, P. S., 1962*a*. "*Bathynella natans*, new to Scotland." *Glasg. Nat.*, **18**, 175–176.

MAITLAND, P. S., 1962*b*. "The fauna of the River Endrick in relation to local water use." *Wat. and Waste Treatm.*, **9**, 78–86.

MAITLAND, P. S., 1963. "*Hemiclepsis marginata* and *Batracobdella paludosa* in Stirlingshire, with notes on the ecology and morphology of the latter species." *Glasg. Nat.*, **18**, 219–227.

MAITLAND, P. S., 1964*a*. "Quantitative studies on the invertebrate fauna of sandy and stony substrates in the River Endrick, Scotland." *Proc. Roy. Soc. Edinb.*, **68**, 277–301.

MAITLAND, P. S., 1964*b*. "A population of Common Carp (*Cyprinus carpio*) in the Loch Lomond district." *Glasg. Nat.*, **18**, 349–350.

MAITLAND, P. S., 1965. "The feeding relationships of Salmon, Trout, Minnows, Stone Loach and Three-spined Sticklebacks in the River Endrick, Scotland." *J. Anim. Ecol.*, **34**, 109–133.

Mann, K. H., 1953. "A revision of the British leeches of the family Glossiphoniidae with a description of *Batracobdella paludosa* (Carena, 1824), a leech new to the British fauna." *Proc. Zool. Soc. Lond.*, **123**, 377–391.

Mann, K. H., 1955. "Some factors influencing the distribution of freshwater leeches in Britain." *Verh. int. Ver. Limnol.*, **12**, 582–587.

Marlier, G., 1951. "La biologie d'un ruisseau de plaine." *Mem. Inst. Sci. Nat. Belg.*, **114**, 1–98.

Martin, C. H., 1907. "Notes on some Oligochaets found on the Scottish Loch Survey." *Proc. Roy. Soc. Edinb.*, **28**, 21–28.

Millais, J. G., 1906. *The mammals of Great Britain and Ireland.* London.

Mills, D. H., 1962. "The Goosander and Red-breasted Merganser as predators of Salmon in Scottish waters." *Sci. Invest. Freshw. Fish. Scot.*, **29**, 1–10.

Mills, D. H., 1964. "The ecology of the young stages of the Atlantic Salmon in the River Bran, Ross-shire." *Sci. Invest. Freshw. Fish. Scot.*, **32**, 1–58.

Moffett, J. W., 1936. "A quantitative study of the bottom fauna in some Utah streams variously affected by erosion." *Bull. Univ. Utah, Biol. Ser.*, **3**, 1–33.

Moon, H. P., 1934. "An investigation of the littoral region of Windermere." *J. Anim. Ecol.*, **3**, 8–28.

Moon, H. P., 1936. "The food of the smolt of *Salmo salar* in the River Avon (Hampshire)." *Ann. Rep. Avon Biol. Res.*, **4**, 85–89.

Moon, H. P., 1937. "Importance of environment on aquatic life." *Ann. Rep. Avon Biol. Res.*, **5**, 24–31.

Moon, H. P., 1938. "Importance of the substratum to the invertebrate animals on which fish feed." *Ann. Rep. Avon Biol. Res.*, **6**, 36–40.

Morgan, N. C., and Egglishaw, H. J., 1964. "A survey of the bottom fauna of streams in the Scottish Highlands. Part 1. Composition of the fauna." *Hydrobiologia*, **25**, 181–211.

Müller, K., 1954. "Investigations on the organic drift in North Swedish streams." *Rep. Inst. Freshw. Res. Drottning.*, **35**, 133–148.

Müller, K., 1955. "Produktionbiologische Untersuchungen in Nordschwedischen Fliessgewässern. Teil 3. Die Bedeutung der Seen und Stillwasserzonen für die Produktion in Fliessgewässern." *Rep. Inst. Freshw. Res. Drottning.*, **36**, 148–162.

Nall, G. H., 1930. *Life of the Sea Trout.* London.

Needham, P. R., 1928. "A net for the capture of stream drift organisms." *Ecology*, **9**, 339–342.

Needham, P. R., 1934. "Quantitative studies of stream bottom foods." *Trans. Amer. Fish Soc.*, **64**, 238–247.

Neill, R. M., 1938. "The food and feeding of the Brown Trout (*Salmo trutta* L.) in relation to the organic environment." *Trans. Roy. Soc. Edinb.*, **59**, 481–520.

Nietzke, G., 1938. "Die Kossau. Hydrobiologische-faunistische Untersuchungen an schleswig-holsteinischen Fliessgewässern." *Arch. Hydrobiol. (Plankt.)*, **32**, 1–74.

Old, M. C., 1932. "Environmental selection of the fresh-water sponges (Spongillidae) of Michigan." *Trans. Amer. Micr. Soc.*, **51**, 129–136.

Oliff, W. D., 1960. "Hydrobiological studies on the Tugela River system. Part 1. The main Tugela River." *Hydrobiologia*, **14**, 281–385.

Pentelow, F. T. K., 1932. "The food of the Brown Trout (*Salmo trutta* L.)." *J. Anim. Ecol.*, **1**, 101–107.

Pentelow, F. T. K., Southgate, B. A., and Bassindale, R., 1933. "The proportion of the sexes and the food of smolts of Salmon and Sea Trout in the Tees estuary." *Fish. Invest. Lond.*, **3**, 11–14.

Percival, E., and Whitehead, H., 1929. "A quantitative study of the fauna of some types of stream-bed." *J. Ecol.*, **17**, 282–314.

PERCIVAL, E., and WHITEHEAD, H., 1930. "Biological survey of the River Wharfe. II. Report on the invertebrate fauna." *J. Ecol.*, **18**, 286–302.

PHILIPSON, G. N., 1954. "The effect of water flow and oxygen concentration on six species of caddis fly (Trichoptera) larvae." *Proc. Zool. Soc. Lond.*, **124**, 547–564.

RASMUSSEN, C. J., 1955. "On the effect of silage juice in Danish streams." *Verh. int. Ver. Limnol.*, **12**, 819–822.

REYNOLDSON, T. B., 1953. "Habitat of *Polycelis felina* (= *cornuta*) and *Crenobia alpina* in the British Isles." *Nature, Lond.*, **171**, 660.

REYNOLDSON, T. B., 1958. "The quantitative ecology of lake-dwelling triclads in Northern Britain." *Oikos*, **9**, 94–138.

RICHARDSON, R. E., 1921. "Bottom and shore fauna of the middle and lower Illinois River." *Bull. Ill. Nat. Hist. Surv.*, **13**, 363–522.

RICHARDSON, R. E., 1929. "The bottom fauna of the middle Illinois River, 1913–1925: its distribution, abundance, valuation and index value in the study of stream pollution." *Bull. Ill. Nat. Hist. Surv.*, **17**, 387–475.

RICKER, W. E., 1934. "An ecological classification of certain Ontario streams." *Univ. Toronto Stud., Biol.*, **37**, 1–114.

RICKER, W. E., 1937. "The food and the food supply of Sockeye Salmon (*Oncorhyncus nerka* Walbaum) in Cultus Lake, British Columbia." *J. Biol. Bd. Can.*, **3**, 450–468.

ROOS, T., 1957. "Studies on upstream migration in adult stream-dwelling insects. I." *Rep. Inst. Freshw. Res. Drottning.*, **38**, 167–193.

ROTHACHER, J. S., 1953. "White Hollow watershed management: 15 years of progress in character of forest, runoff and streamflow." *J. For.*, **51**, 731–738.

SCHMITZ, W., 1955. "Physiographische Aspekte der limnologischen Fliessgewässertypen." *Arch. Hydriobiol. (Plankt.)*, **22**, 510–523.

SCHUMANN, F., 1928. "Experimentelle Untersuchungen über die Bedeutung einiger Salze, insbesondere des kohlensauren Kalkes, für Gammariden und ihren Einfluss auf deren Häutungsphysiologie und Lebensmöglichkeit." *Zool. Jb.*, **44**, 623–704.

SCHWOERBEL, J., 1961. "Die Bedeutung der Wasser milben für die biozönotische Gliederung." *Verh. int. Ver. Limnol.*, **14**, 355–361.

SCOTT, D., 1958. "Ecological studies on the Trichoptera of the River Dean, Cheshire." *Arch. Hydrobiol. (Plankt.)*, **54**, 340–392.

SCOTT, D. B. C., 1963. "Reproduction in female *Phoxinus*." *Ph.D. Thesis, University of Glasgow*.

SCOTT, T., and BROWN, A., 1901. "The marine and freshwater fishes" in Elliot, G. F. S., Laurie, M., and Murdoch, J. B., 1901. *"Fauna, flora and geology of the Clyde area."* Glasgow.

SLACK, H. D., 1934. "The winter food of Brown Trout (*Salmo trutta* L.)." *J. Anim. Ecol.*, **3**, 105–108.

SLACK, H. D., 1957a. "The topography of the lake." *Glasg. Univ. Publ., Stud. Loch Lomond*, **1**, 4–13.

SLACK, H. D., 1957b. "Physical and chemical data." *Glasg. Univ. Publ., Stud. Loch Lomond*, **1**, 14–26.

SLACK, H. D., 1957c. "The fauna of the lake." *Glasg. Univ. Publ., Stud. Loch Lomond*, **1**, 33–48.

SMART, J., 1944. "The British Simuliidae, with keys to the species in the adult, pupal and larval stage." *Sci. Publ. Freshw. Biol. Ass.*, **9**, 1–57.

SMITH, J. G., 1896. *Strathendrick and its inhabitants from early times.* Glasgow.

SMYLY, W. J. P., 1955. "On the biology of the Stone-loach, *Nemacheilus barbatula* (L.)." *J. Anim. Ecol.*, **24**, 167–186.

SOONG, M. K., 1938. "Preliminary notes on the food of young Trout and Salmon parr." *Ann. Rep. Avon Biol. Res.*, **6**, 34–35.

SPERBER, C., 1950. "A guide for the determination of European Naididae." *Zool. Bidr.*, *Uppsala*, **29**, 45–78.

STEINMANN, P., 1907. "Die Tierwelt der Gebirgsbäche, eine faunistisch-biologische Studie." *Ann. Biol. lacust.*, **2**, 30–163.

STEINMANN, P., 1915. *Praktikum der Süsswasserbiologie. 1. Teil: Die Organismen des fliessendem Wassers.* Berlin.

STEUSLOFF, U., 1938. "Beiträge zur Ökologie nordwestdeutscher Spongilliden." *Arch. Hydrobiol.* (*Plankt.*), **33**, 309–338.

STUART, T. A., 1953a. "Water currents through permeable gravels and their significance to spawning Salmonids, etc." *Nature, Lond.*, **172**, 407–408.

STUART, T. A., 1953b. "Spawning migration, reproduction and young stages of Loch Trout (*Salmo trutta* L.)." *Sci. Invest. Freshw. Fish. Scot.*, **5**, 1–39.

STUART, T. A., 1959. "The influence of drainage works, levees, dykes, dredging, etc., on the aquatic environment and stocks." *Athens Proc. 7th Tech. Meet. I.U.C.N.*, **4**, 337–345.

STUART, T. A., 1962. "The leaping behaviour of Salmon and Trout at falls and obstructions." *Sci. Invest. Freshw. Fish. Scot.*, **28**, 1–46.

SURBER, E. W., 1936. "Rainbow Trout and bottom fauna production in one mile of stream." *Trans Amer. Fish Soc.*, **66**, 193–202.

SWIFT, D. R., 1961. "The annual growth-rate cycle in Brown Trout (*Salmo trutta* Linn.) and its cause." *J. Exp. Biol.*, **38**, 595–604.

SWORD, J., 1908. "The vertebrate fauna of the King's Park, Stirling." *Trans. Stirling Nat. Hist. Soc.*, **8**, 123–152.

SWYNNERTON, G. H., and WORTHINGTON, E. B., 1940. "Note on the food of fish in Haweswater (Westmorland)." *J. Anim. Ecol.*, **9**, 183–187.

TANSLEY, A. G., 1939. *The British Islands and their vegetation.* Cambridge.

THIENEMANN, A., 1912. "Der Bergbach des Sauerlands. Faunistisch-biologische Untersuchungen." *Hydrobiologia*, *Suppl.*, **4**, 1–125.

THOMAS, J. D., 1962. "The food and growth of Brown Trout (*Salmo trutta* L.) and its feeding relationships with the Salmon parr (*Salmo salar* L.) and the Eel (*Anguilla anguilla* (L.)) in the River Teifi, West Wales." *J. Anim. Ecol.*, **31**, 175–205.

URE, D., 1795. "Parish of Killearn." *The Statistical Account of Scotland*, **16**, 100–129.

WEEREKOON, A. C. J., 1956. "Studies on the biology of Loch Lomond. 1. The benthos of Auchentullich Bay." *Bull. Ceylon Fish.*, **7**, 1–94.

WESTLAKE, D. F., 1959. "The effects of organisms on pollution." *Proc. Linn. Soc. Lond.*, **170**, 171–172.

WHITEHEAD, H., 1935. "An ecological study of the invertebrate fauna of a chalk stream near Great Driffield, Yorkshire." *J. Anim. Ecol.*, **4**, 58–78.

WOOD, I., 1954. *Loch Lomond and its Salmon.* Glasgow.